OF AMERICA
POPULATION

CANADA

Me.
913,774
31,040

533,242
9,024

377,747
9,278

Vt. **N.H.**

N.Y.
14,830,192
47,929

4,690,514
7,907

Mass.
R.I.
791,896
1,058

Conn.
2,007,280
4,899

inn.
982,483
,009

Wis.
3,434,575
56,154

Mich.
6,371,766
57,022

Pa.
10,498,012
45,045

N.J.
4,835,329
7,522

Ia.
,621,073
55,986

Ill.
8,712,176
55,947

Ind.
3,934,224
36,205

Ohio
7,946,627
41,122

W. Va.
2,005,552
24,090

Md.

Del. 318,085
1,978

Va.
3,318,680
39,899

2,343,001
9,887

Mo.
3,954,653
69,270

Ky.
2,944,806
40,109

D.C.
802,178
61

Ark.
1,909,511
52,725

Tenn.
3,291,718 *41,961*

N.C.
4,061,929
49,142

Miss.
2,178,914
47,420

Ala.
3,061,743
51,078

Ga.
3,444,578
58,518

S.C.
2,117,027
30,594

La.
2,683,516
45,177

Fla.
2,771,305
54.262

250

NORTH AMERICA

By the same Author

AN INTRODUCTION TO ECONOMIC GEOGRAPHY

HOOVER DAM, THE COLORADO RIVER AND LAKE MEAD. *To the left and in the distance is the State of Nevada; to the right, Arizona.*

NORTH AMERICA

N. J. G. POUNDS
M.A., Ph.D.

Professor of Geography, Indiana University
Formerly Tutor, Fitzwilliam House, Cambridge

JOHN MURRAY
FIFTY ALBEMARLE STREET
LONDON

First published October 1955
Reprinted April 1956

Printed in Great Britain by
Latimer, Trend & Co Ltd, Plymouth
and published by John Murray (Publishers) Ltd

Foreword

THIS book has been written as a text for Advanced Level candidates by one who may claim some acquaintance with both the English sixth former and the examinations that he has to face, and also with the American scene. The writer hopes that it will make some contribution towards the understanding in England of American people and their problems.

He wishes to express his thanks to Miss Barbara Bonner, librarian of the English-Speaking Union in London, for some valuable suggestions for the "literary" reading list; to his wife for her assistance in preparing the manuscript; and to the various firms and organizations that have kindly supplied photographs.

N. J. G. POUNDS

Cambridge,
England.
June, 1955

Acknowledgements

Thanks are due to the following who have kindly given permission to reproduce photographs:

U.S. Bureau of Reclamation (*frontispiece* and *p. 134*); Port of New York Authority (*pp. 54 and 55*); Pennsylvania Turnpike Trust (*p. 70*); Chamber of Commerce, Pittsburgh (*p. 71, top*); New Orleans *News* (*p. 71, bottom*); United States Steel Corporation (*p. 102, top*); American Iron and Steel Institute (*p. 102, bottom*); Standard Oil Company, N.J. (*p. 103, top; p. 118; p. 119; p. 135; p. 150, top; p. 151, top*); Trans World Airlines (*p. 150, bottom; p. 151, bottom; p. 166, bottom*); Chamber of Commerce, San Francisco (*p. 166, top*); Office d'Initiative Économique et Touristique, Montreal (*p. 167, bottom*); Ontario Hydro (*p. 182*); Canadian Pacific Railway (*p. 183*).

Contents

Illustrations

Maps and Diagrams

ix

— I —

Opening up a Continent

In the early years of the sixteenth century, a mapmaker, Waldsee-müller, was at work on a new map of the known world. He had heard something of recent voyages westwards across the Atlantic and of lands newly discovered on the far side. Stories had reached him about these regions sufficiently detailed for him to represent their coastline on his map. But the New World lacked a name. Waldsee-müller seems to have based his map in part at least on the narrative of one, *Amerigo* Vespucci, who claimed, a few years before, to have navigated a ship to the New World and to have explored much of its coast. So the unknown West was named after him: "America". This name, which has since remained attached to the two continents of the New World, first appeared on Waldseemüller's map in 1507.

The New World had been first reached from Europe fifteen years before by Christopher Columbus. In the course of four voyages, between 1492 and 1503, he explored the islands of the West Indies and parts of the neighbouring coasts of Central America. He was followed by a host of adventurers, most of them Spanish, who crossed the Isthmus of Panama to the Pacific Ocean, invaded and conquered Mexico, pressed southwards into the Andean country of South America, and sent expeditions deep into the heart of North America.

We cannot say with certainty at what point the North American continent was first visited by Europeans. It is probable, if not alto-gether certain, that in the tenth and eleventh centuries the Norsemen, sailing by way of Iceland and Greenland, had made a landfall on the inhospitable coast between Labrador and New England. The descrip-tions they gave may have encouraged settlers but were hardly a true account of the geography of these areas. Norsemen may indeed have settled here, and some people to-day claim to have discovered evidence of a prolonged occupation of parts of North America by the Norsemen.

But these settlers, if indeed they ever existed, did not maintain contact with either Greenland or their European homes. The colony in Greenland continued for several centuries, but seems to have become extinct during the fifteenth century.

In 1497 John Cabot, of Bristol, sailed to the west. He reached, almost certainly, Newfoundland, and may have visited neighbouring coasts, but we know nothing of the second voyage which he made to these regions in the following year. Soon afterwards Portuguese and French sailors began to frequent the seas off Newfoundland, attracted by the wealth of fish, which has not ceased since then to be an important source of food for Europe.

Gradually Spanish sailors and Portuguese and French fishermen revealed the nature of the eastern coasts of North America. In 1534 Jacques Cartier, a member of a Breton fishing community, reached Newfoundland, and then passed on through the Strait of Belle Isle, examined the coasts of Labrador and Newfoundland, and returned to France by way of the Cabot Strait (fig. 1). There was little to tempt Europeans in the lands which Cartier saw. Though it was early June, his voyage was hindered by ice. He wrote of Labrador that it was "composed of stones and horrible rugged rocks; for along the whole of the north shore I did not see one cart-load of earth and yet I landed in many places. Except at Blanc Sablon there is nothing but moss and short, stunted shrub. In fine I am rather inclined to believe that this is the land God gave to Cain."[1] He greatly regretted that the soil was not "as good as the harbours" along this indented fjord coast.

Nevertheless, he returned the following year, sailing up the St. Lawrence estuary to a point near the present site of Quebec. The river stretches south-westwards, and the voyage upstream brought Cartier into warmer latitudes. From his base near Quebec, Cartier explored the valley as far up as the Lachine Rapids and the "mountain" of *Mont Réal* (Montreal). From the summit we had "a view of the land for more than thirty leagues. . . . Towards the north there is a range of mountains (i.e. the Laurentians) running east and west, and another range (i.e. the foothills of the Adirondack Mountains) to the south. Between these ranges lies the finest land it is possible to see, being arable, level and flat. . . ." This area is now one of the most populous and well cultivated areas of Canada.

In the meanwhile the Spaniards had entered the North American continent from the south. The voyages of Cabot and Cartier had been made hazardous by ice and stormy seas. A barrier of desert protected

[1] H. P. Biggars, *The Voyages of Jacques Cartier* (Ottawa, 1924), p. 22.

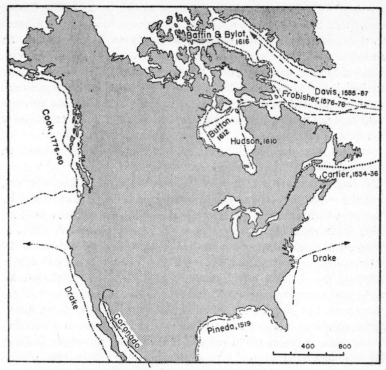

Fig. 1. THE EARLY VOYAGES OF DISCOVERY

the continent on the south-west, and along its southern shores were swamps, difficult and dangerous to navigate. Cabez de Vaca, in the years 1528 to 1536 made the long journey from Florida to Mexico, keeping to the north of the coastal swamps[1] and marshes. The report of De Vaca encouraged others to explore the continent. In 1539 Hernando de Soto moved northwards from the Florida coast. His object was gold. He travelled northwards across Georgia and South Carolina. He kept above the level of the coast plain, on the Piedmont, or plateau, which slopes seawards from the Appalachian Mountains. Indians advised him to travel to the west. Keeping to the Piedmont, his party skirted the mountains, crossed either northern Alabama or Tennessee and reached the Mississippi River. He crossed the river and reached the hills of Missouri (the Ozarks), which he found to be "very rough

---

[1] In American terminology the word "swamp" is given to marshy country in which trees grow. The terms "marsh" and "bog" denote an absence of trees.

country".[1] De Soto despaired of finding wealth by travelling further to the west through this poor upland. An attempt to escape southwards to the Gulf of Mexico was defeated by the "great bogs" (that is, the swamps of Louisiana); a further attempt to travel west or south-west to Mexico only took the party "through lands which became more sterile" (i.e. Oklahoma or Texas). Finally, a renewed attempt to sail down the Mississippi and through the swamps to the sea was crowned with success, though De Soto had died somewhere along the banks of the great river.

A year after the departure of De Soto's expedition, Francisco de Coronado set out to explore the country lying to the north of Mexico. The desert lands around the head of the Gulf of California were visited, and the expedition moved northwards until its path was blocked by "a river which seemed . . . more than three or four leagues . . . across. . . . This country was elevated and full of low twisted pines, very cold. . . . They spent three days on this bank looking for a passage down to the river, which looked from above as if the water was six feet across, although the Indians said it was half a league wide."[2] This was the great gorge of the Colorado River. It blocked their progress, and the party turned to the east, crossed the great Front Range of the Rocky Mountains, and dropped down to the plains of Kansas and northern Texas. Here they saw the huge herds of bison and the Plains Indians. But they failed to find the foremost object of their search, the precious metals, and, disappointed, they turned back towards Mexico.

By the middle of the sixteenth century much of the southern and north-eastern parts of North America were known to Europeans. Sailors had passed along the Atlantic coast and its main features were being represented with some pretension to accuracy on the maps of the period. Though few could have penetrated inland, except perhaps up some of the greater rivers, a favourable picture was generally given of the coastal lands all the way from Cape Cod to Florida. Settlers were attracted by the supposed beauty and riches of this land, and some were rudely disillusioned by the diseases of the coastal swamps in the south, by the Indian attacks and by the severe winters further north.

But many who came to the New World regarded it only as a barrier to their progress to the supposedly richer lands of Asia. Magellan sailed around the southern extremity of South America. The Spaniards

---

[1] *Narratives of the Career of Hernando de Soto*, ed. E. G. Bourne (London, 1905).

[2] F. W. Hodge and T. H. Lewis, *Spanish Explorers in the Southern United States* (Hakluyt Society, 1849), p. 309.

crossed the Isthmus of Panama and built fresh ships on the Pacific coast. The English tried to sail around the northern limit of the continent: Martin Frobisher got no further than Baffin Land. John Davis sailed far to the north along the western coast of Greenland. Henry Hudson penetrated the deep gulf which bears his name. Baffin, Bylot, Foxe and James all ran into the barrier of ice which seals permanently this northern waterway against the passage of man.

The Early Settlement of the Atlantic Coast. Towards the end of the sixteenth century or in the early years of the seventeenth three areas along the Atlantic seaboard came to be settled by people of European stock. The new land had much that was familiar to the immigrants. "In most cases", in the words of Carl Sauer, "the colonists were at no loss to identify the native plants and animals which they found on the western side of the Atlantic. It would be impossible, indeed, to cross an ocean anywhere else and find as little that is unfamiliar in nature on the opposite side. In all the lands of earliest colonization, from Massachusetts Bay south to Virginia, flora and fauna were closely related to those in the European homeland and indicated to the settlers that they were still under familiar skies and seasons. . . ."

But there were differences. "This was indeed a lustier land to which the settlers had come, a land of hotter summers and colder winters, of brighter and hotter sun and more tempestuous rain, and land suited to and provided with a greater variety of vegetation than the homelands of Europe. . . ."[1]

Early in the seventeenth century the French began to settle in the St. Lawrence Valley, the advantages of which had been reported on by Cartier. It was a land of hot summers and long, severe winters. European methods of agriculture had to be modified. Grain crops were grown and cattle reared, but fishing and the trapping of wild, fur-bearing animals offered a means of livelihood of no less importance. Along the banks of the St. Lawrence River, from the sea up to Montreal, the French settlers laid out their long, strip-like holdings, each with a narrow frontage on the river, a pattern of land holding that still remains to-day. Settlements were also made on the islands near the St. Lawrence mouth, on Prince Edward Island and Cape Breton Island, where the somewhat milder winters made agriculture more practicable.

In contrast with the region chosen by the French, the earliest

---

[1] Carl O. Sauer, "The Settlement of the Humid East", in *Climate and Men*, (U.S. Department of Agriculture, 1941), p. 159.

English settlements were in an area that was almost sub-tropical. The
Elizabethan settlements made on the coast of Virginia were not maintained, but in 1607 a new and permanent settlement was established
at Jamestown, on the James River, a tributary of the Chesapeake. The
park-like country, with its splendid trees and rich vegetation, gave
every prospect of success for the settlers, but the climate was hotter than
that to which they had been accustomed, the diseases more virulent
and the Indians hostile. They adapted themselves slowly to a diet consisting largely of corn (maize), the staple Indian food. The settlement
barely survived the difficulties of its early years, and its success was
really assured only when tobacco and sugar became the staple crops
and slaves were introduced to cultivate them.

The settlers of Maryland followed quickly on those of Virginia (1634),
and south of Virginia colonies were established in North Carolina
(1663), South Carolina (1670) and, lastly, in Georgia (1733). The first
villages were established along the tidewater, where rice and sugar
could be grown. As the settlers spread inland they passed on to the
rather higher land of the Piedmont, lightly wooded with a soil that
gave good crops of cotton and tobacco. The cultivation of sugar, rice,
cotton and tobacco demanded heavy labour in the hot sun, which the
white settlers could perform only with difficulty, if at all. Furthermore,
many of the settlers had little inclination to do manual work whether
the sun was hot or not. Early in the seventeenth century African slaves
had been introduced, and their numbers increased with their usefulness. The southern "states", from Maryland to Georgia came to depend
on slave labour for the production of sub-tropical crops. These crops
could be marketed in Europe. Tobacco, sugar and cotton were shipped
in increasing quantities from the ports of Chesapeake Bay and from
Charleston and Savannah, and in return the colonists imported manu-
actured goods from England. A commercial link was thus forged between the southern states and north-western Europe that even to-day
has not been wholly severed.

Intermediate between the French settlements along the St. Lawrence
River and the English settlements in the south was the group of New
England settlers. Their choice of Massachusetts was a result rather of
the lack of skill of their pilot than of their own volition. Their objective
was a more southerly point on the American coast. The Pilgrim Fathers
established their Plymouth colony in 1621. Their environment was, in
the American phrase, "rugged", and they lacked the advantage of a
friendly and helpful European government, able to send them supplies.
They had to contend with the cold and snowy New England winter, to

accustom themselves to Indian "corn" as their chief diet, and to defend themselves against the hostile Indians of the hinterland.

Other groups joined the Pilgrims, though often differing from them on the finer shades of biblical interpretation. They spread along the coast westwards from Cape Cod, up the Connecticut Valley and northwards along the rocky coast of Maine. Slaves were unnecessary in New England. The settlers were more inured to hardship and labour than the gentlemen of Virginia. The plantation crops that were the mainstay of the south would not grow here. The settlements were self-sufficing, and had little trade with England because there was very little which either side desired to exchange. The hostility which the New Englander felt towards England's meddling colonial policy was never tempered by the economic necessity of selling goods in the English market. Distrust ripened into hostility, and hostility led to rebellion.

The area between New England and Maryland came later to be occupied by a miscellaneous group of Europeans, small in number though very important in the development of America. A group of Dutch founded New Amsterdam (New York), at the mouth of the river which Henry Hudson had recently explored, thinking it a passage to the Pacific, and which now bore his name. Groups of Swedes, Finns and Germans settled in New Jersey and Delaware, and in 1681 William Penn established the Quaker colony at Philadelphia, which still anachronistically bears the title of "city of brotherly love". Penn's colony grew into the Commonwealth of Pennsylvania.

In the mid-eighteenth century the European settlers, the Spaniards of the south-west excepted, were still confined to the tract of low land, nowhere much more than 200 miles wide, between the Appalachian Mountains and the sea. Towards the north, the French of Canada had, as it were, turned the flank of these mountains by following the St. Lawrence Valley, but their furthermost settlement was no more than some 250 miles from the Atlantic Ocean.

The total number of settlers was small. In the whole French-settled area there were in the mid-eighteenth century probably no more than 20,000 white people. The population of the English colonies was larger, but at the same time probably did not exceed one and a quarter millions, including the negro population. Of these, about 60 per cent were of English descent, and a further 12 per cent Scottish or Irish. Thus three-quarters of the total were English-speaking. The rest were made up of Germans fleeing from the ravaged Palatinate or Rhineland, of Dutch, Swedes, French and Finns.

The native population of the North American continent, north, at

B

Indians

least, of Mexico, was Indian. They are commonly pictured as the inveterate foe of the white man, strong in numbers and savagely resisting his progress into the interior. This is hardly true. Their numbers were small. Along the whole Atlantic seaboard, from New England to Florida, there were, at the time of the earliest English settlements, no more than about 125,000 Indians. Eastern Canada certainly contained no more than 50,000, and the continent as a whole probably had only about two millions.

In the east, most of the Indians at some time practised agriculture, but they also relied heavily on the produce of their hunting and fishing. They seem to have lived in small villages commonly placed on rising ground near a river. "About theire houses they have commonly square plotts of cleared grownd, which serve them for gardens, some one hundred, some two hundred foote square, wherein they sowe their tobacco, pumpons (pumpkins), and a fruit like unto a musk millino (melon) . . . in the tyme of theire huntings they leave their habitations, and gather themselves into companyes . . . where they passe the tyme with hunting and fowling up towards the mountains, by the heads of the rivers, wher indeed there is plentye of game."[1] The Indians moved their villages frequently both in search of game and because they quickly exhausted the fertility of the soil and were obliged to make fresh clearings.

Though there were frequent and bloodthirsty wars between the white settlers and the Indians, the newcomers nevertheless learned much from the native population. They took over the native crops, especially corn, squash, pumpkin and artichoke. The Indians also guided the white settlers in selecting the edible wild fruits and berries. Indians worked for the whites, assisted them when they migrated and guided them into the mountainous hinterland of the early settlements.

The Road West. Along the western skyline of the seaboard colonies lay the Appalachian Mountains, ridge behind ridge, forested to their summits, and offering few easy routes across them to the interior. Between the ridges, which lay roughly parallel to the Atlantic coast, there were only narrow tracts of flat land capable of cultivation. Rivers broke across the ridges, often by narrow gorges up which movement was very difficult though generally not impossible. The Appalachians were not a barrier to human movement, but they formed a broad belt of trackless forest and mountain across which there was little inducement to

[1] William Strachey, *History of Travails into Virginia Britannia*, quoted in Ralph Brown, *The Historical Geography of the United States* (New York, 1949), p. 12.

move as long as there was enough good soil to cultivate along the sea-board plain.

During the eighteenth century, however, a growing land-hunger was apparent. Parties of settlers pressed up the valleys of the Appalachians and occupied the narrow strips of lowland between the Appalachian ridges. Settlers made their own way westward by any route they might

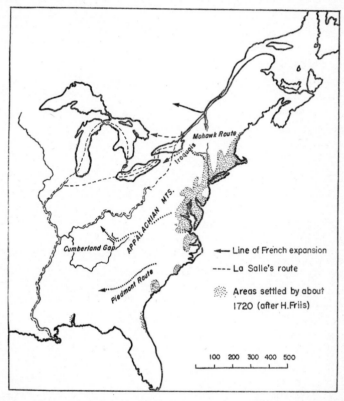

Fig. 2. THE EARLY JOURNEYS INTO THE NORTH AMERICAN CONTINENT

learn of from the Indians or chance to discover themselves, but five routes stood out as particularly important because they reduced the burden of travel.

1. The first and easiest was occupied by the French who had sailed up the St. Lawrence and, when they had reached Lake Ontario, had got round behind the mountains. From their early base at Montreal, the French settlers, led by Samuel de Champlain, explored the valleys

of the upper St. Lawrence and its tributaries. Once they had reached the Great Lakes, the French explorers were able to advance quickly by water. French missionaries and trappers soon acquired a working knowledge of the whole Great Lakes region, from Lake Ontario to the "upper lake" or Lake Superior. Those unevenly matched groups, the Jesuits and the *coureurs du bois*, converted the Indians and bought the pelts they hunted. In 1672 Joliet and Marquette, both of them Jesuits, reached the Mississippi River by following the Fox and the Wisconsin Rivers. Nine years later La Salle reached the Mississippi and followed it to the Gulf of Mexico.

These French travellers had been greatly assisted by portages, which derived from earlier river-capture. These permitted them to cross from the drainage basin of the Great Lakes to the drainage basin of the Mississippi, carrying their canoes sometimes only for a mile or two if the level of the rivers was high.

They explored a vast area, and the knowledge which they accumulated was ultimately incorporated in maps of the region, but they were unable to make good their occupation of the land. There were not enough French settlers. Their forts or trading posts were scattered too thinly over the land for them to make a deep and permanent impression. A few French names, like Detroit, Prairie du Chien, La Crosse and Vincennes, remain to-day as evidence of French occupance. A French settlement pattern, remotely resembling that along the St. Lawrence Valley, can be detected at points along the Mississippi Valley, but the French settlers have been gone for close on two centuries and their language is never spoken.

2. Behind the harbour and city of New York, the Hudson River opened a corridor into the interior between the New England mountains to the east and the Catskill Mountains to the west. About 150 miles north of New York the Mohawk River joins the Hudson from the west, and provides a low-level route almost to the shores of Lake Ontario. The route lay open and inviting, yet it was not until the middle years of the eighteenth century that the first settlements were made along the Mohawk. Some were deterred by the cold and snowy winters, but the greatest obstacle was the powerful Indian confederation of the Iroquois which lay astride this route. It was not until its strength was broken late in the eighteenth century that movement westward by this route became important. The easiest trans-Appalachian route in the United States was thus the last to be opened up, but once the flood-gate of the Iroquois had been removed the stream of settlers flowed west,

spreading along the southern shores of the Great Lakes and over the plains of Ohio and Indiana.

3. Inland from Philadelphia and Baltimore, the Appalachian ridges are crossed by the Susquehanna and Potomac Rivers, and their tributaries, which provide valley routes that are wider and more easily traversed than most. Furthermore, not far beyond their headwaters, the tributaries of the Ohio took their rise and flowed westward. A number of routes was used across what is now western Pennsylvania and West Virginia. Several converged on the future site of Pittsburgh, where the Allegheny and the Monongahela join to make the Ohio River, whose broad waters could bear the rough boats of the early settlers westwards towards the Mississippi.

4. In Virginia several of the Appalachian ridges diminish in height and breadth and the valleys between them become proportionately wider. Early in the eighteenth century pioneers moved south-westwards between these ridges. In this way the Great Valley of Virginia was settled, but the mountains became gradually higher and the valleys narrower. Settlements were less frequent, and then they ceased. About the mid-eighteenth century the Cumberland Gap was discovered across the last of the ridges—the so-called Cumberland Mountains— and the road lay open to the fertile plains of Kentucky. Within a few years a stream of settlers passed up the Appalachian valleys, through the Gap and then fanned out over Tennessee and Kentucky. Some went north to the Ohio River and then on into southern Indiana and Illinois. Abraham Lincoln's family came by this route. His grandfather had crossed the mountains with the early wave of settlers and had settled in Kentucky. His father had then migrated into southern Indiana and then into Illinois, where Lincoln rose to fame as a lawyer and politician. Others went west to the Cumberland River, which they followed westward across Tennessee. The use of the Cumberland Gap explains why the States of Tennessee and Kentucky were the first trans-Appalachian states to become populous enough to enter the Union.

5. The Appalachian Mountains sink gradually in northern Georgia and Alabama into hills which are in turn lost amid the undulations of the Piedmont. This plateau stretches without interruption from Maryland to Mississippi. In general it was lightly wooded and had a good soil. Yet the limit of white settlement remained for many decades along the Savannah River of Georgia (see fig. 2). Lying across the line of advance were the swamps of southern Georgia; Indian tribes, notably

the Cherokee, Choctaw, Chickasaw and Creek Indians, were tenacious fighters and, above all, the Spaniards held Florida and the Gulf coast and claimed an ill-defined area of the hinterland.

At the end of the century the growing numerical strength of the American settlers and the diminishing power of Spain combined with an increasing demand for cotton to force an opening across the South. The Spanish-held territory was whittled away, and in 1819 the United States purchased Florida, all that remained of it.

The way now lay open for the cotton kingdom to spread across the south, from Georgia to the Mississippi River. The boom in the European—especially the English—cotton industry, the invention in 1794 of a gin which could remove the seeds from the bolls of the short-staple cotton that was grown in the interior, and an abundant supply of slave labour took the fields of cotton across the Old South.

By the end of the eighteenth century a population map of the white settlers would have shown five westward projections, corresponding with the five gaps through or around the Appalachian chain. Most progress had been made in the one extending west from the Cumberland Gap, but movement along the roads which converged on Pittsburgh and through the Mohawk Valley was increasingly vigorous.

In the course of the Seven Years' War, which ended in 1763, French rule of Canada was exchanged for British. Twenty years later the British relinquished their last possession within the present territory of the United States, and the boundary between the United States and Canada was established. In 1776, the thirteen States which comprised the original "Union" declared their political independence, and their population, welling through the Appalachian Mountains, was now beginning to people the Mid-West, and there were established the States of Kentucky in 1792, Tennessee in 1796, and Ohio in 1803. The plains of Ohio and northern Indiana, the rich "blue grass" country of Kentucky and the rolling cotton and tobacco country of Tennessee were slowly filling up. Dirt roads were laid out. This vast new country was surveyed and divided into "township" units, each six miles square. Each township was divided into thirty-six sections of a single square mile, and groups of townships were organized into counties.

> We squared the country for liberty, laying it off
> With the posts plumb on the section lines and the fences
> Following due west from the creeks of Kentucky
> To the counties bigger than Delaware: christened for congressmen. . . .

Townships were sold, either entire or by sections, to prospective settlers. Roads were planned, enclosing not only each township but also each section. This gridiron pattern of roads survives over much of the Mid-West and West, though locally the broken terrain compelled the road-makers to depart from the simple pattern prescribed and often many of the roads were found to be unnecessary and were never built.

Cotton was the mainstay of the southern settlers; tobacco and corn (maize) of those in the middle states, and wheat and corn across the north. The north to south flowing system of the Mississippi carried the wheat and hogs, the dried tobacco and the huge bales of cotton down to the Gulf. In the early years of the nineteenth century the great river became a busy place as the "flatboats" were replaced by the shallow-draught, unwieldy "stern-paddlers", chugging up and down the Mississippi and Ohio Rivers. Mark Twain has left an unforgettable picture[1] of the varied life along the river, when it was the only artery channelling the produce of this rapidly expanding frontier: the treacherous and changing river with bordering forests, swamps and "cut-offs"; its colourful towns where the cotton was loaded: Memphis, Vicksburg, Natchez, and the "Metropolis of the South", New Orleans itself, lying below the level of the river for much of the year, protected by only the "frail breastwork of earth" of the levées.

In Canada the westward movement of the frontier was less rapid. English-speaking settlers came to the upper St. Lawrence Valley and peopled the Lake Peninsula of Ontario, where the climate was moderated somewhat by the proximity of the lakes. But along the northern shore of Lake Huron and Lake Superior stretched the Laurentian Shield. This region of ancient rocks had been partially denuded of its soils during the Ice Age. Its mineral wealth had not yet been prospected, and its softwood forests were at this date too remote from the coast to have much value. For many decades its chief wealth was held to consist in its fur-bearing animals, which were trapped and their skins sold to the agents of the Hudson's Bay Company, whose commercial supremacy over this northern wilderness was scarcely challenged.

The West. The Mississippi had set a temporary halt to the westward march of settlement. The river was a serious obstacle and beyond it were Indians more hostile than those of the east. Trees thinned away towards the borders of the prairie; the climate became more severe, or

---

[1] Especially in *Life on the Mississippi*, but also in the novels, *Huckleberry Finn* and *Tom Sawyer*.

at least seemed so to the pioneers in this land devoid of both fuel and a wind-break to take the edge off the northern blizzard. The thick prairie turf was tough, cut only with the greatest difficulty by the wooden plough of the early settlers. The wheat lands of Kansas, Nebraska and the Dakotas lay far in the future.

Though prospects of immediate settlement were slight, a number of expeditions set out to explore the West and to report on the possibility of agricultural developments. The earliest of the important expeditions actually started from the Hudson Bay in northern Canada. Samuel Hearne, a servant of the company, reached the Great Slave Lake and the Coppermine River, which flows to the Arctic Ocean, in 1771. In 1789 Alexander Mackenzie journeyed down the much bigger river which bears his name almost to its junction with the northern ocean. Four years later he travelled up the Peace River, a western tributary of the Mackenzie, crossed the Rocky Mountain divide and reached the Pacific Ocean, the first man to cross the continent from east to west.

During the next generation numerous explorers began the work of filling in the gaps in the current knowledge of north-western Canada. By the mid-nineteenth century, travellers, most of them in the service of the Hudson's Bay Company, had accumulated a very considerable body of knowledge of this territory.

On the American side of the boundary, the work of exploring the West was pushed ahead no less assiduously and with considerable financial help from the Federal Government. In 1803 money was appropriated for the work, and Meriwether Lewis and William Clark set out from St. Louis, at the junction of the Missouri River with the Mississippi. At this time popular imagination located the "Great American Desert" in what are now the High Plains. Beyond them rose the "Stony Mountains" from which rivers descended to the Pacific. The task of the explorers was to clear up the uncertainty regarding these regions, to discover a navigable waterway which could be used by commerce to the far West and to reveal the economic potentialities of the region.

The right bank tributaries of the Mississippi appeared to provide routes, but the rivers were an uncertain help. A description of the Platte River in Nebraska is typical also of most of the others. It is "broad, shoal and not navigable, I believe, even during the prevalence of its floods. It is exceedingly winding for more than half the distance from its heading sources, and flows principally through sandy barrens, and over a sandy bed, occasionally interrupted by rocks. At times it is almost dry, and may be forded in particular places with almost dry feet; while, at others, it is difficult to conceive of the volume of water that seeks a level, with astonishing rapidity, through its wide-cut channels."[1]

Over much of the area between the Mississippi River and the Rocky Mountains, the vegetation was a grassy steppe. The forest that covered the eastern parts thinned away towards the west, until trees were limited to the fringe of cotton woods that bordered the rivers. Between the rivers lay the Prairie, undulating or level. "Sometimes it glares in the sun, an expanse of hot, bare sand; sometimes it was veiled by long coarse grass. Skulls and whitening bones of buffalo (i.e. the bison) were scattered everywhere; the ground was tracked by myriads of them, and often covered with the circular indentations where the bulls had wallowed in the hot weather. The river itself runs through the midst, a thin sheet of rapid, turbid water, half a mile wide and scarcely two feet deep. Its low banks, for the most part without a bush or a tree, are of loose sand, with which the stream is so charged that it grates on the teeth in drinking."[2]   At night the wolves, coyotes and prairie dogs disturbed the quiet, and at all times there was danger from the Prairie Indians.

Such was the country through which Lewis and Clark travelled in 1803 and 1804. They followed the Missouri River north-westwards, reached the Rocky Mountains in territory that is now Montana, crossed the divide, and, following first the Snake River and then the Columbia, they reached the sea.

Many fur-trappers and traders followed along the route of Lewis and Clark. They explored the Bighorn Mountains and discovered the South Pass, easiest of all the Rocky Mountain crossings; they crossed the Great Basin, the arid plateau that lies to the west of the Rocky Mountains, saw the Great Salt Lake, and reached the great gorge of the Colorado River.

In 1806–7 Zebulon M. Pike had travelled up the Arkansas River, southwards, through Santa Fé, to Mexico and back by way of Texas. In 1819 another expedition was sent west by the Federal Government. S. H. Long went up the Platte Valley, explored the Rocky Mountains of Colorado and returned by way of the Arkansas River. With the journeys of Frémont, beginning in 1838 and continuing until 1853, the main features of the geography of the West were made known.

The exploration of the American West brought with it two immediate

[1] John D. Hunter, *Memoirs of a Captivity among the Indians of North America* (1823), quoted in E. W. Gilbert, p. 53–4.
[2] Francis Parkman, *The Oregon Trail*, first published 1847. Penguin edition, 1949, p. 62.

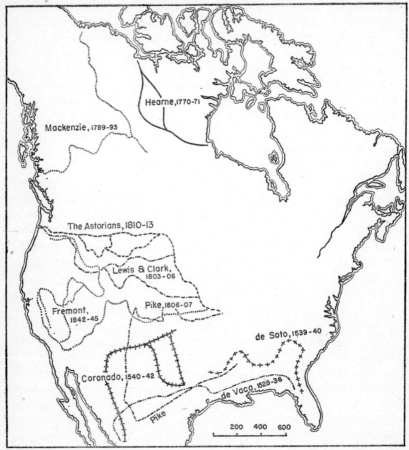

Fig. 3. THE EXPLORATION OF THE AMERICAN WEST

consequences: contact—and conflict—with the Mexicans and the development of ranching on the Prairies. Despite the barrier of desert and
steppe which lay along the northern border of Mexico, Spanish settlers
had penetrated territory which to-day makes up the American South-
West. The Rio Grande Valley, northwards from El Paso to Santa Fé
was well settled, and there were mission stations and trading posts set
up by the Spaniards in southern Texas, Arizona and California. The
abundance of Spanish place-names in these regions to-day witnesses to
the formerly widespread Spanish settlements. The exploration of the
South-West had revealed the fact that these areas could be reached
more easily from St. Louis, by way of the Kansas River, than from any

point in present-day Mexico. Very early in the nineteenth century, merchants began to make the long journey along the trail that led to Santa Fé. Then further trails were developed across the desert country to the settlements in southern California.

The second development was that of the "Cattle Kingdom". The grasslands of southern Texas were well suited to the rearing of cattle. In 1821 the first ranching settlement was established; others quickly followed. The territory was then part of the Mexican republic, against whose inefficient and corrupt government the settlers rebelled in 1835 and established their independence. The "Lone-star Republic"[1] of Texas lasted until 1844 when it was absorbed into the United States.

The acquisition of Texas prepared the way for the American conquest of the very much larger area which lay between the Rio Grande and the Pacific. This area, most of it desert or scrubland with "oases" along its major rivers, had been thinly settled by Spanish missions. It had been explored by Frémont and now American settlers were beginning to filter into the region. War with Mexico broke out over the question of the boundary of Texas and ended with the United States annexing the whole territory in 1848. Five years later, American territory was rounded off by the Gadsden Purchase.

The American absorption of Texas prepared the way for the range cattle industry. The range was the great, unfenced grassland, where the winters were not unduly severe and the lush grasses could support immense herds of the long-horned "Texas-Mexican" cattle. This industry gradually extended northwards from Texas, along the eastern foot of the Rocky Mountains, to Wyoming, Montana and the Canadian provinces of Saskatchewan and Alberta, whither the great herds of cattle followed the Chisholm or some other trail. In the words of one of the cowboy songs:

> . . . Git along little dogies (steers),
> For you know Wyoming will be your new home.

In the meanwhile the slow drift of settlers westwards towards the Pacific Ocean was increasing to a flood. In 1849, gold was discovered at Sutter's Creek in the Great Valley of California. Settlers, eager to participate in the wild scramble for gold, now came in their thousands, across the Prairies in their "covered wagons" or "prairie schooners", as they were called, on horseback and even on foot. They faced the dangers from the still only partially subdued Indians, from the wolves on the plains and the bears in the mountains, from hunger and thirst every-

[1] So called from the single star on the flag of the short-lived republic.

where along the long trail from the Mississippi to California. Some
stopped and made their homes along the route; many succumbed to the
hazards of the journey, but enough survived them to raise the white
population of California from 15,000 in 1848 to 380,000 in 1860 and to
justify its admission as one more state in the American Union. A very
few even discovered gold.

Other gold rushes followed: to the Fraser River valley in the Canadian
Rockies, to Nevada, Colorado, Idaho, Montana and, last and perhaps
the most colourful, the rush to the gold-fields of the Klondyke in
Alaska.

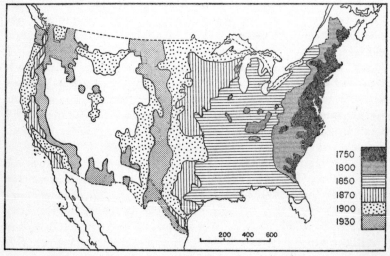

1750
1800
1850
1870
1900
1930

200   400   600

Fig. 4. STAGES IN THE SETTLEMENT OF THE UNITED STATES

But not all settlers came west in a search for gold. Some wanted good
crop land, others ranch land, yet others merely wanted to practise
some new religion or to experiment with some novel Utopia of their
own design. In this way the Mormons established their homes close to
the arid shores of the Great Salt Lake of Utah and here, in the spirit of
the early Israelites, they conquered the harsh environment by their
labours and built up a social system as successful as it was strange.

The Frontier. No one can understand America without understanding the "Frontier". It was "the outer edge of advancing settlement, the
meeting point of savagery and civilization, the zone where civilization
entered the wilderness. . . ."[1] The Frontier has been defined officially

[1] R. A. Billington, *Westward Expansion, a History of the American Frontier* (New York,
1949), p. 3.

as a belt of territory having not less than two, nor more than six persons per square mile. It spread slowly across the continent, and in 1890 the Bureau of Census declared that, as far as the United States were concerned, the Frontier had been so broken up by areas of denser settlement that it could not be said to exist any more. The continent was filling up with people. In that year the population of the United States was 62,947,700 and of Canada about 4,833,239. The only large areas of sparsely populated or uninhabited land were the deserts of the West and the forests and tundra of the North.

The influence of the Frontier has gone deep into American life. The frontiersman was an individualist; he was coarse and materialistic, practical and adaptable. His way of life had no room for tradition; the only aristocrats of the Frontier were those who had achieved this position by their personal prowess—the Daniel Boones, Jesse Jameses and Kit Carsons. The Frontier was thus democratic, in counting family or inheritance for nothing. The Frontier, secondly, was lawless. Settlers moved faster than the judiciary and police. The only law in the early mining camp or on the range was the rough justice of a bunch of miners or of cowhands. The self-help of the Frontier is reflected in the contempt for law that has only too frequently characterized life in many other parts of the United States besides the Frontier. The materialism of the Frontier has carried with it a distrust of what is intellectual and only too often a dislike for the aesthetic. American education remains more practical than that in Europe, and those academic pursuits which in Europe carry the greatest prestige are in general held in small esteem in America.

The Frontier, lastly, turned the gaze of Americans towards the heart of their own continent. Settlers along the Atlantic seaboard remained interested in Europe, where they sold their cotton and wheat, but to the frontiersman, engrossed in his struggle against a harsh environment, Europe was merely a distant land of which he knew little and cared not at all. That attitude of mind which we call Isolationism was natural to him, and it takes more than two World Wars and a threat from Soviet Russia to break it down.

— 2 —

The Regions of North America

In 1890 there was much sparsely peopled land in the United States, but no great open spaces devoid of settlers. This was not true of Canada. The whole Canadian North was virtually unsettled, and over parts of the western plains and Rocky Mountains the inhabitants were very few. Nevertheless, the main lineaments of the continent were familiar. There were areas of the Canadian Arctic never visited by the white man, but, as a whole, the continent was mapped. The direction of almost every river, the position of nearly all mountain ranges, was known. There were reports on climate, soil and native vegetation. The natural wealth of every major area had been assessed and its suitability for settlement evaluated. Let us pause, then, and look at the physical lineaments of this continent.

THE RELIEF OF NORTH AMERICA. Continental North America has an area of 9,213,000 square miles, to which must be added a further 882,500 for Newfoundland and Greenland, which is commonly regarded as part of North America. This is a good deal more than twice the area of Europe, even including European Russia. North America extends through 58 degrees of latitude. Its most southerly point, the Keys, or small islands off the southern extremity of Florida, lie at 25° N.; its most northerly is only 450 miles from the Pole. The longitudinal extent of North America is even greater. Eastern Greenland is only 20 degrees west of Greenwich. Western Alaska lies in a longitude of 170° W. In terms of *time*, these extremes are no less than ten hours apart. The main body of the continent is, however, very much narrower. It is 70 degrees (or 3,200 miles) from the St. Lawrence mouth in eastern Canada, to Vancouver Island in western.

In terms of relief, the continent divides itself quite simply into three large divisions. All lie roughly in a north-to-south direction: in the east is a belt of mountainous country, with a bordering coastal plain. In the centre, reaching all the way from the Gulf of Mexico to the Arctic Ocean, is a great area of plain or plateau. The western third of the continent is occupied by the serrated ridges of the Rocky Mountains and of the other chains which together make up the belt of high and rugged country bordering the Pacific Ocean.

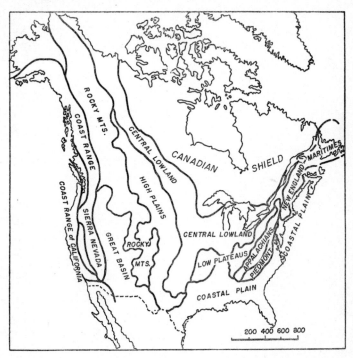

Fig. 5. PHYSICAL REGIONS OF NORTH AMERICA

The Appalachian Mountains and Laurentides. The Appalachians form the more southerly part of this mountainous belt. It is, we have seen (page 8), made up of a great number of parallel ranges; none of them particularly high, but generally steep-sided, forested and offering a serious obstacle to transverse movement. There might be as many as a dozen such ranges, lying one behind the other. They are broken up by transverse river valleys, some straight like the Hudson or the lower Potomac; others deep, narrow and tortuous. The Appalachians are generally held to terminate in the Catskill Mountains.

North of the Catskills, beyond the valley of the Mohawk, lie the

Adirondack Mountains, geologically a part of the Laurentian Shield; to the east, beyond the Hudson valley are the Taconic, the Green and the White Mountains of New England. These reach away through Maine and into Canada where they culminate in the Shickshock Mountains of the Gaspé Peninsula of Quebec.

Between the Appalachians and the Atlantic Ocean is a coastal plain; wide in the south, but narrowing northwards until it is only about fifty miles across in New England, then widening again in New Brunswick and Nova Scotia.

The direction of the Appalachians is continued in Newfoundland, where the mountains have been worn down to a maze of rounded hills. But north of the estuary of the St. Lawrence the land rises steeply to the Laurentian "Shield". This vast area of hard rock also underlies a great deal of the great plain which lies to the west, but here, in eastern Canada, it attains a far greater altitude. Its rounded, forested hills overlook the St. Lawrence Valley, which appears as a tenuous oasis framed by the Laurentides and the most northerly ranges of the Appalachian system.

The Great Plains. It is customary, though by no means correct, to refer to the vast region lying between the Appalachians and the Rockies as the Great Plains. The region is very far from level, and towards the west its altitude entitles it to the name of "plateau". In the north it is underlain by the ancient rocks of the Laurentian Shield. These have been glaciated; in parts they have been scraped bare of soil and hollows have been formed, now filled with lake or bog. Towards the south these ancient rocks dip beneath younger rocks, and also beneath a cover of glacial deposits (see page 98). The glacial plains, which make up much of the "Mid-West" of the United States, are varied in soil though generally level or gently rolling. Inliers of older rocks occasionally break through the surface of the drift, producing rugged islands which sometimes rise steeply from this sea of glacial deposits.

To south and west the glacial deposits terminate, and a more uneven terrain appears. In general it is one of rounded hills, which become higher towards the west, and the rivers are more deeply incised. The rocks that compose it are intermediate in geological age between those of the Shield and the glacial drifts. They consist of bedded limestones, sands and shales. But locally these beds have been worn away and the older rocks show through, producing areas of greater altitude and rougher terrain. The Ozark and Ouachita Mountains are one of the largest of such areas.

The drainage of this region is southwards to the Gulf. The Mississippi and its great tributaries, the Missouri and Ohio, have built up broad plains of alluvium across which they snake their way, not infrequently inundating the level lands which border them (see p. 127). These alluvial plains broaden southwards until they stretch along the whole Gulf Coast, from Florida to Texas.

The Rocky Mountains. This name should strictly be given only to the more easterly range, which rises abruptly from the plains. It is high, reaching altitudes of over 14,000 feet in Colorado. For long distances it is difficult to cross, and, as we have seen, it constituted a severe barrier to the early explorers. For much of their distance, however, the mountains merely mark the eastern margin of the high plateau which covers the western states of the U.S.A. This plateau, usually called the Great Basin (see p. 144) lies generally at a height of over 5,000 feet. On the west it is bordered by the Sierra Nevada, Cascade and Canadian Coast Ranges. Its surface is itself broken by many short ranges, lying roughly from north to south, parallel with the mountains that border the plateau.

The more southerly parts of the plateau are drained southwards by the Colorado and Rio Grande Rivers. The central area has no outlet to the sea; the rivers, many of them flowing only irregularly, discharge into salt lakes and swamps. The more northerly part is drained by the Columbia River which breaks through the western ranges to the Pacific Ocean. The Great Continental Divide, which separates the rivers flowing to the Atlantic from those discharging to the Pacific, lies roughly along the more easterly range of mountains, the Rocky Mountains themselves.

As the Canadian boundary is approached, the more easterly and the more westerly ranges draw together; the plateau character of the intervening area disappears, and a complex series of mountain ranges, lying roughly parallel to the Pacific coast, stretches north-westwards into Alaska, where they terminate on the shores of the Bering Sea.

The Ice Age. The relief of the more northerly parts of the continent was greatly influenced by the Pleistocene glaciation. The ice appears to have advanced southwards from the region of Hudson Bay no less than five times. Its earliest advances were the most extensive, and the "older drift" was spread as far south in the Central Plains as the Missouri and Ohio Rivers. In fact, the present courses of these rivers in part originated as the beds of marginal streams flowing along the edge of the ice. But apart from such disturbances of drainage, the older glaciations have left little trace. The newer, however, have laid down a thick cover of drift over the northern Great Plains and Great Lakes regions. Here the terrain is almost wholly the product of the glaciation, except for one small area, the so-called "driftless" area of Wisconsin, which was enclosed but never covered by the ice. The roughness of this small area shows how the glacial deposits have levelled up the surface of the land, eased the problem of transportation and in general improved the soil.

The changes in drainage that resulted from the Ice Age were greatest in the area of the Great Lakes, and the consequences of these changes are important to-day. As the margin of the ice shrank back towards the north, the ice continued to cover the lower St. Lawrence Valley while most of the Lakes region was free. Marginal lakes were formed. At first they discharged southwards to the Mississippi and Ohio. Then a lower outlet offered by way of the Mohawk and Hudson Valleys; lastly the St. Lawrence Valley itself became clear of ice, and offered the lowest outlet to the sea. Thus the present drainage pattern evolved, but there remained the valleys of the former rivers that once carried the drainage in other directions. They were marshy depressions lying ready for the modern canal builder. The Erie Canal (see p. 52) was cut along the Mohawk outlet, and the former outlet direct to the Mississippi is to-day again in use. The small Chicago River has been turned back on itself; instead of flowing into Lake Michigan, it now carries the water of the lake—and also the effluvia of Chicago—westwards by way of the glacial overflow to the Illinois River and thus to the Mississippi. There is now a through navigation all the way from the St. Lawrence River to the mouth of the Mississippi.

West of the Great Lakes other lakes formed along the border of the ice sheet. Largest and, from our point of view, the most important of these was a vast tract of water, known in retrospect as Lake Agassiz, which covered parts of present-day Minnesota and North Dakota and the Canadian province of Manitoba. The pre-glacial drainage of this area had been eastwards and northwards. The escape of water was cut off by the great continental ice sheet and the lake accumulated. A limit to its growth was set by a spillway south to the Mississippi. After the retreat of the ice, the lake shrank away, and to-day it is represented by Lake Winnipeg and other scattered lakes of Manitoba. But the vanished waters have left behind a wide, level and deep deposit of rich alluvium. This occupies the Red River Valley as well as most of southern Manitoba, and supports the great spring wheat belt of the United States and the rich farming area of Manitoba.

Elsewhere in North America, the moister conditions of the Ice Age led to the formation of lakes. A vast lake filled what is to-day the desert basin of Utah, and many lakes lay along the western margin of the Great Basin, fed by the extensive snow-fields of the Sierras. Their legacy to us is the extensive areas of alluvial soil, sometimes salt impregnated, often in need of irrigation, but generally fertile and productive.

THE CLIMATE OF NORTH AMERICA. This continent is, in the words of Carl Sauer which we have already quoted, 'a land of hotter summers and colder winters, of brighter and hotter sun and more tempestuous rain . . . than the homelands of Europe".[1] In so vast a

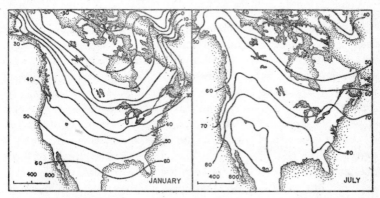

Fig. 6. SUMMER AND WINTER TEMPERATURE, IN DEGREES FAHRENHEIT, IN NORTH AMERICA

land area a great variety of climate is to be expected. What settlers had not always reckoned with was the violence of its climate; the suddenness of its changes; the severity of its extremes. Torrential rains and dust storms, winter blizzards and spring floods indeed make this "a lustier land" than Europe.

The climate at any time and at any place in the continent is due to the air mass which is dominant at the me. The air masses that influence the climate are (1) the Polar air, which comes in from the North Pacific, northern Canada or the North Atlantic. It is cool or cold, and if it comes off the ocean is usually damp; and (2) the Tropical air which moves northwards from the Gulf of Mexico or from tropical latitudes in either the Pacific or Atlantic Oceans. These air masses are warm or

[1] *Climate and Man*, p. 159.

hot. They tend often to be humid, as, moving into cooler latitudes, their relative humidity becomes greater.

Air masses from these two sources alternate over much of the United States and southern Canada. Those who are accustomed to the gentle fluctuations in England between the north-east and south-west winds, can have no realization of the violence of the change in North America. In the midst of the continent a mild winter day, with a temperature in the 40 degrees or even 50 degrees can be followed by one up 50 degrees colder, as a cold front moves over, and Arctic air replaces tropical. Conversely in summer the hot and humid air from the Gulf extends far north into Canada, bringing a heat wave, with temperatures in the 90 degrees and over to much of the continent. People long for the cooling breath of the Arctic air as much as, in winter, they dread its approach.

The sudden and extreme changes of climate are one of the strongest influences on human life in the North American continent. In most parts the house has to be heated and insulated to withstand the zero temperatures which occur at intervals during three or four months of the year; it has to be ventilated to make it inhabitable during the summer. One sees, beside the railroad tracks, a row of snow ploughs, whose presence goes oddly with the summer temperature of nearly 100 degrees, or one notices alongside the main roads, when the corn is ripening in the blistering August heat, the low wind-breaks of short stakes and wire which in winter keep the snow drifts off the highway. In summer one sees along the Mississippi or Missouri or Ohio high concrete levées, towering fifty or more feet above the quiet stream; one would hardly believe that in winter and spring they scarcely suffice to hold back the raging water. It is, indeed, "a lustier land to which the settlers had come"; the wonder is that, before the days of central heating and air conditioning, without modern houses and fast transport, they managed to stay.

But climate is far from uniform. Ocean currents, mountain ranges and plateaux, lakes and distance from equator or pole all have their effects in bringing about a variation of climate over the continent. On the basis of these differences, it is possible to divide the continent into eight climatic regions:[1]

1. *Tundra and Ice Cap.* This region extends across the extreme north of the continent from Labrador to Alaska (see fig. 7), and covers the Arctic islands and Greenland. Summers are cool and short; winters,

---

[1] The regional classification here adopted is that of Professor Glenn T. Trewartha.

long and and extremely cold. Precipitation, most of which comes in the form of snow, is relatively small. The long period of freezing weather inhibits plant growth, and the short summer, despite the long hours of sunshine which in June and July amount to nearly twenty-four in the day, is inadequate to promote a rich vegetation cover or to permit the cultivation of crops. The vegetation of most of the region is low growing

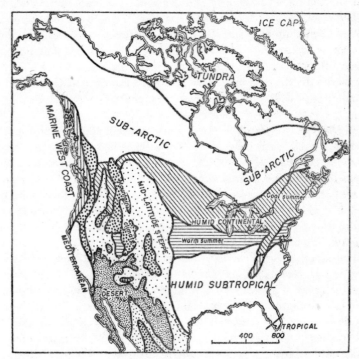

Fig. 7. CLIMATIC REGIONS OF NORTH AMERICA

plants, stunted conifers and, more often, lichens and mosses. The soil is often thin and usually sour; the subsoil is frozen for most, if not all the year, and the natural drainage of the soil is inhibited. Animal life is restricted to small fur-bearing animals which hibernate for much of the winter and to the larger animals which are able to migrate south-wards into the shelter of the forest belt in winter. The seal, walrus and polar bear breed along the coasts. Human life is limited to the few small migratory groups of Eskimo and the occasional trapper or prospector or the trading emissary of the Hudson's Bay Company.

2. *Sub-Arctic Region.* Forming a broad belt across the continent to

the south of the Tundra is the coniferous or softwood forest. Spruce, fir and larch predominate. Towards the southern margin of the forest belt the trees are tall and well grown, and are interspersed with deciduous trees. Northwards the trees diminish in size until, in the Tundra, they become only dwarfed replicas of themselves.

Winter is scarcely less severe in the forest belt than in the Tundra, but the summers are longer, and the total insolation is greater. The soil is generally poor, leached and podsolized. There is no autumn leaf-fall and little humus is added. But in a few favoured places, where the climate is less severe, and the soil better, agriculture is practised and hardy, quick-maturing crops are grown. In the Peace River Valley of northern Alberta and the "Clay Belt" of Ontario and Quebec small colonies of settled cultivators have been established.

3. *Humid Continental Climate.* South-eastern Canada and north-eastern United States have a climate distinguished at the same time by seasonal extremes of temperature and considerable humidity. It is usual to divide this region, according to the length and temperature of the summer into the "warm summer" and "cool summer" variants. But throughout the humid Continental region the winters are less extreme and the summers longer and less cold than in the sub-polar climate. Fig. 6 illustrates the range of temperature.

Towards the north the vegetation consists of broad-leafed hardwood trees, interspersed with conifers which often cover the higher ground and the areas of poorer soil. To the south, conifers are extensive only in the mountains. In Canada and the north-eastern United States, maple and hemlock predominate; to the south, chestnut, oak and yellow poplar (tulip tree) and, across the Mid-West, oak and hickory. Much of the native forest, especially in the valleys of the Appalachians and New England, along the Atlantic seaboard and over the plains of the Mid-West, has been cleared to make way for agriculture, but enough remains to make this a predominantly wooded region. In late August the maple trees along the St. Lawrence begin to turn first yellow and then flaming red. A sea of red gradually spreads southwards into the hills of Vermont and New Hampshire. It flows along the Appalachian ridges, lighting them with shades of yellow, brown and crimson, and then reaches out across the Mid-West until the last trees die out on the edges of the Prairie.

The long drawn-out fall, with warm days and cool nights, is one of the few rewards for bearing with the extremes of summer and winter. But by late October most of the leaves have fallen. The temperatures drop rapidly. The football season, which had opened in September on sun-baked fields, ends in November on a frozen ground in a flurry of snow. Arctic air has extended across the humid Continental region, and, with only occasional intermissions, will remain until spring. But at intervals during the winter the warm tropical air will edge northwards, and along the southern limits of the region it intrudes quite often. Snow comes and goes; periods of freezing or even "zero" weather alternate with conditions which even in England would be called mild. As the temperature rises above and then falls below freezing-point, there is a danger of freezing rain and glazed frost, with treacherous highways and a high accident rate. In most places, some time during the winter, there is a heavy fall of snow which brings all movement to a temporary standstill.

Winter ends almost as suddenly as it began. A few balmy days in March or April with a south wind bringing tropical air over the region; a rise in temperature of 15 or 20 degrees, and summer has come. There is a short-lived glory of the fresh green of the maple and oak, and of the flowers of the redbud, dogwood, catalpa and magnolia. Then in the heat of June and July the ground becomes parched and plants wilt. Torrential rain accompanies the summer thunderstorms; the temperature drops a few degrees, and climbs again to its next peak—and the next thunderstorm. In the "dog-days" of August and early September, one longs again for the "Indian summer" of late September and October.

Soils over much of this region can rarely be classed as good. Generally they are leached, though the leaf fall has added humus and raised them considerably above the level of the podsols. They are commonly classed as "grey-brown podsolic" soils, with pure podsols occurring in mountains.

4. *Humid Sub-tropical Climate.* To the south of the Humid Continental region, the winters become a great deal milder and summers a little hotter. Spells of freezing weather become rare or short. The January average is over 45 degrees along most of the coast and rises in southern Florida to over 65 degrees. But the summer averages rise to over 80 degrees, and few summers pass without temperatures of well over 100 degrees. The general mildness of the southern winters is interrupted on rare occasions when arctic air makes its way almost to the Gulf, bringing a cold which seems even more extreme than it is by contrast with the prevailing mildness. The orange-growers of Florida have always to be prepared to face a spell of freezing weather.

Under the generally mild and moist conditions, rocks disintegrate quickly to form soil, but the humus is itself quickly decomposed and dispersed. The product is a soil leached like the northern podsols, but often deeper. Though there are many exceptions the region as a whole is not particularly fertile or productive. The apparent richness of its vegetation is due rather to the warmth, the moisture and the long growing season than to any intrinsic values of the soil.

In the northern parts of this region the hardwood forests, which characterized the region of humid continental climate, thin away, and are replaced by stands of southern pine. The long and the short leaf, slash and loblolly pines are the dominant trees over the whole area from the lower Mississippi Valley eastwards to the Atlantic coast. Around the coast and stretching up the valleys of most rivers are swamps. The southern swamp is an area of stagnant water with a thick growth of rushes and other marsh plants, trees, draped with the swaying masses of grey-brown Spanish moss, and a rich reptile and insect life. The cypress is the characteristic tree of the swamp; its swollen base and "knees" are one of its most familiar features. The southern swamps cover a very large area—some 142,200 square miles. So far, little progress has been made in draining them, and some parts of the swamps of South Carolina and Georgia are actually preserved as wild life refuges. In Florida, the swamps assume an even more tropical character, and in southern Florida tropical mangrove swamps are to be found.

5. *The Prairie Region.* Towards the west, both the humid continental and the humid sub-tropical regions become drier and their temperatures somewhat more extreme. The trees become fewer, their stands less frequent and, when the white man first came, he found the land covered with tall grass. The diminution of rainfall is an important reason for the disappearance of the forest, though along the forest edge the primitive Indian practice of burning the forest probably had the effect of further limiting its extent. The tall grasslands extend far into the humid regions of the east (compare figs. 8 and 35) and in much of the tall grass area trees will grow well if planted. "Why prairies should be found in such a climate has long been a matter of speculation. Given prairie to start with, it is not hard to imagine that the dense, vigorous grass, with the help of fire, could have kept trees from invading. A good prairie fire would destroy any tree seedlings that might come up, with no permanent injury to the grass."[1] The region is, topo-

---

[1] *Grass: Yearbook of Agriculture, 1948* (U.S. Dept. of Agriculture), pp. 47–8.

graphically, a plateau rising very gently from the Mississippi Valley to the foot of the Rocky Mountains. The rivers, which flow eastwards from the mountains, have carved shallow valleys. Thin strips of woodland—cottonwood, ash, elder and hickory—lie along the watercourses, and provide the only source of fuel and building material in the Prairies. As the rainfall continues to diminish, the tall grass of the eastern Prairies gives place to the short, drier grass of the western. To-day the area of tall grass is under crops: cotton, corn, wheat. Parts of the drier grasslands are also cultivated, but in the main these remain to-day the home of the cattle breeder and rancher.

Over most of the grassland the rate of evaporation is high, especially in summer, when it greatly exceeds the precipitation. In these conditions there is little or no leaching. Indeed the reverse takes place; lime and other soluble soil constituents are drawn upwards to the surface, where they are left by the evaporation of soil moisture. The result is the formation of a soil in which humus, with the addition of lime and other soil-forming materials, make a concentrated but shallow surface layer, dark in colour and rich in fertility. This is the *chernozem* which makes the Prairies the productive wheat and corn lands that they are. Towards the margin of the Prairies, the *chernozem* becomes degraded. To the west and south it passes, in areas of increasing aridity into the red and brown soils of the deserts, in which the volume of humus is very small indeed. To the north it passes into the northern podsols.

6. *Steppe and Desert Climates of the West.* The western third of the continent is an area of varied relief, with high mountain ranges, separated by plateaux. Most of the region lies within the rain shadow of the Sierra Nevada, the Cascade Mountains and Canadian Rockies and Coast Range, and much of the plateau areas has an annual rainfall of less than 10 inches, and parts of the Mojave Desert of southern California are almost rainless. The rainfall comes mostly in the winter, but towards the north an increasing proportion falls in other parts of the year. The driest and hottest regions of the south-west of the United States experience an unreliable but sometimes considerable rainfall from summer thunderstorms which are often of exceptional violence.

It is difficult to generalize regarding vegetation and soil in a region as varied as this. The mountain ranges, which experience a heavier precipitation than the plateau areas, have stands of coniferous woodland: in the south a short and scrubby growth of juniper and pinyon; further to the north, pine and spruce. The lower-lying plateau areas, with their scanty and unreliable rainfall support only a scattered growth of bush. In the hotter and drier south, the creosote bush predominates, and the tall, branching cactus gives an exotic appearance to the landscape. Further north is sagebrush. In areas of inland drainage, which cover much of Nevada and Utah, a salt-impregnated soil is almost devoid of vegetation.

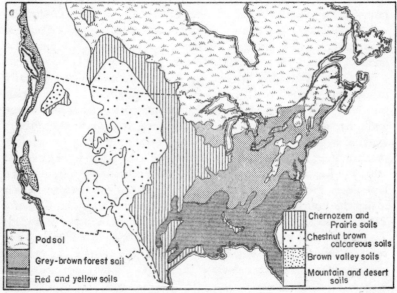

Podsol

Grey-brown forest soil

Red and yellow soils

Chernozem and Prairie soils

Chestnut brown calcareous soils

Brown valley soils

Mountain and desert soils

Fig. 8. SOIL TYPES IN NORTH AMERICA

The thin soils of the arid regions are almost entirely lacking in humus; there is too little plant growth to supply organic matter to the soil. On the other hand, the small rainfall and strong evaporation have the effect of bringing the soluble minerals to the surface, and parts of the arid West are potentially fertile if only water can be brought to them. At the present time, the great rivers of the West, the Columbia, Snake, Colorado and others, are being dammed and made to supply water to this thirsty land.

The Mediterranean Region of California. Readers of *The Grapes of Wrath* will remember how the Joad family, migrating from their wind-blown, run-down farm in Oklahoma to the brighter prospects of California, came over the Tehachapi Pass and looked down into the great valley of California.[1] The contrast between the arid lands and California is extreme, and not a few migrants to California have looked upon it

[1] See below, p. 141.

as a "promised land", full of "milk and honey". California is the North American exemplification of Mediterranean climate. Its summers are long and very hot. It is often forgotten that this objective of so many hopes shares with Arizona the unwelcome distinction of having the highest recorded temperatures in the United States. Winters are warm and, occasionally uncomfortably hot. As the rainfall comes chiefly in the months from November to March, the autumn, winter and spring are the seasons of growth, when the evergreen shrubs put on their bright colours, and fields and gardens are vivid with magnolia, bougain-villaea, and the crimson of the poinsettya, which, with careful pub-licity, has been made the Christmas flower of much of the United States.

Summers are dry, and agriculture difficult without the use of irriga-tion, which, thanks to the many streams that descend from the Sierra Nevada, is widely available. A climate which suits the Mediterranean flowering shrubs, suits also the orange, lemon, grape-vine and peach. Orchards and irrigated crop land lies along the valleys and over the plain. The hill ridges support only a growth of stunted, drought-resist-ing trees, resembling the *maquis* of southern Europe, with the cedars and the giant red firs in the mountains. In the Sierra Nevada are small stands of the giant sequoia or "bigtree", one of the most publicized and least widespread of all American trees.

The soils of the Mediterranean region do not differ greatly from those of the arid regions. They are yellow and brown soils, rather poor in humus and, except where they can be irrigated and manured, better suited to tree than field crops.

The Pacific North-West. This is the only climatic region of North America in which an Englishman would feel at home, though even here he might regard the amount of snow as somewhat excessive and the frequency of severe storms from the Pacific Ocean as too great. The climate, termed "Marine West Coast", has winters which are mild, though cooler and wetter than those of California, and summers which are amongst the coolest in the continent. This climatic region is, how-ever, one of the least extensive. It borders the Pacific Ocean, from the limits of Mediterranean climate in the south to the sub-arctic region in the north, and it extends inland until, behind the barrier of the moun-tain ranges, the climate becomes too dry and too extreme to be classed as "marine".

The vegetation of this region is chiefly coniferous. The Douglas fir forms vast stands which cover much of the region. They reach up the western flanks of the rain-soaked mountains until they pass over, like the sub-polar forests, into a thin cover of Tundra-like vegetation. The soils, as is to be expected in an area with so great a rainfall and so little evaporation, are leached and poor, resembling the podsols of the more northerly regions.

Grass, which has not been conspicuous in the two regions last considered, here grows as richly as in England. The climate, too wet for many field crops to grow, is well suited to meadow, and in the narrow valleys that separate the ranges dairy farming becomes important.

REGIONS OF NORTH AMERICA. In this chapter we have considered four distributional patterns, each of which is of basic importance in understanding the geography of the continent; that of relief, of climate, of soil and of vegetation. We notice that, unfortunately for our understanding of them, these patterns have little in common, and though climate, soil and vegetation are all three closely linked, the patterns which they make on the map are not the same. To these four, we shall add one further regional pattern. This derives in part from the physical elements we have considered, but it owes most to the history of the continent, to the traditions and practices of the immigrant peoples, to the conditions of the world market over a long period of time, to the ways in which the settlers have reacted to the conditions, both local and physical and also remote, economic or political, which have influenced them.

Fig. 9. REGIONAL DIVISIONS USED FOR THE CHAPTERS OF THIS BOOK

We have the New England region, where early settlement, Puritan background and continuous occupance of the soil have given it a character distinct from that of other regions. We have the Atlantic seaboard, also settled at a relatively early date, but developing a commerce in a few agricultural products. We have the Mid-West, settled in the early nineteenth century by pioneers from the east, traditionally independent, assertive, isolationist and more American than the Americans themselves. Then there is the South, kni together still by the vanished slave economy and the hammer-blows of the northern armies during the Civil War of the 1860's. Beyond the Mid-West and the South is the West, the Prairie states from Texas to Montana, where some of the romance of the vanished "frontier" still remains; then the colourful mountain states with the splendours of nature in the Grand Canyon and Yellowstone and the scarcely less astounding achievements of man, like the Hoover Dam and Bingham Canyon copper mine. Lastly there there is the Pacific Coast, scene of the most vigorous growth of population and industry in recent years, as the United States becomes a Pacific as well as Atlantic Ocean power.

Each of these "human" regions is the subject of a separate chapter. Though some of these regions may be said to stretch across the international boundary into Canada, the Dominion is considered in three separate chapters: the eastern or Maritime Provinces, together with Newfoundland and the St. Lawrence Valley; secondly, the Prairie and Rocky Mountain Provinces; and lastly the Canadian North.

Before turning to a detailed consideration of each of these regions, let us review briefly the development of Canada and the United States in the present century.

— 3 —

The Continent and its Resources

THE North American continent is endowed perhaps a little above the average with the natural resources: soil, fuel and minerals. So great did the reserves appear that extravagant misuse over a period of generations did not seem dangerous or even unwise. Only during the last generation has the American nation awakened with something of a shock to the fact that most of these natural resources are not renewable and can be used only once.

THE LAND. Earliest of these resources to be used was the land. The American Indians do not seem to have made much impression on the resources of the continent. Relative to its size they were few in number; they cleared only very small areas of forest, and their corn patches were far from large. With the coming of the white man the destruction—or at least the extravagant use of resources—spread. The westward movement of settlers in the eighteenth and nineteenth century was not only due to the pressure of their numbers. It owed much to their desire for virgin soil that could be cultivated without the use of fertilizers. With a whole continent before them they may be pardoned for thinking it no abuse to burn forest, take a few crops from the soil enriched by the ashes, and then move on to forests new. They could not envisage the expansion of population that has taken place; nor did they realize that, in the violent climate of the eastern United States, the topsoil, deprived of its vegetation cover, would soon be removed by wind or water.

Furthermore, the crops cultivated by the early settlers were exhausting to the soil. Tobacco land requires many years to recover after each crop, and the cotton crop, in the course of two centuries, cut a broad swathe through the South from the Carolinas to Texas, leaving exhausted and eroded soils and an impoverished tenantry.

Further to the north, corn, taken over from the Indians, became the

36

staple crop and chief food of the white man. Corn was grown in New England, in the Appalachian states and in the Mid-West. It was fed to man and beast. It cropped heavily and did not exhaust the soil like cotton and tobacco, but where summers were dry or cool the corn did not grow well. In Canada it was replaced by rye and oats, and as settlers moved into the dry lands of the western plains it was replaced by wheat.

Cultivation of the Prairie was more difficult than that of the humid East. The climate was more severe and less reliable. The black soil was rich enough, but it supported a thick turf with a matted root system, difficult enough to cut with a steel spade; impossible to break with the primitive wooden plough of the early settlers. The "plough that broke the plains" was a steel plough. Armed with this new tool, settlers spread across the Mississippi, and into Kansas, Nebraska and the Dakotas. They broke the plains; indeed, they ploughed them up over far too wide an area. The railroad had crept up on them; boats were plying on the Mississippi and Missouri; back east, as well as in Europe, a growing population demanded more and more bread. Wheat prices rose, and the steel plough bit ever deeper into the high western plains. Each successive boom drove it further, until at last a combination of low prices during a depression of exceptional severity—that of the 1930s—and the physical consequences of cultivating the dry grasslands drove them back. The wind was left to strip the abandoned fields.

In the meanwhile, wheat farming pressed forward towards its northern margin. Here a limit was set by the length of the growing season. The plant geneticists have produced strains of wheat capable of maturing in ever diminishing periods of time; wheat growing progressed from the plains of North Dakota into those of Manitoba; from Manitoba into Saskatchewan, and is now practised in the Peace River Valley, in a latitude of more than 55° N., with a growing season of considerably under a hundred days.

In the present century agriculture has advanced in a new direction. It had gone to the boundaries—and beyond them—of normally cultivable land. It has now invaded the dry lands of the West and has prospered with the help of irrigation. A limit is set to this expansion by the volume of water in the western rivers, but this limit is far from being reached. At present there is a very active interest in using to the full the water resources of the continent.

Thus were developed the agricultural resources of the continent. The harm done by the hasty and ill-considered developments of earlier generations is being remedied. Soil conservation is seriously studied and actively practised. In some states no one may teach in the public school system who has not studied, in addition to other specialized subjects, the "conservation of natural resources". The improvement and restoration of the soil is an essential part of the great reclamation project of the south-east, the Tennessee Valley Authority, and it is prominent in the plans for the control and development of the Missouri Valley. In hilly areas one sees the plough following the contours of the hill; even ploughing alternate strips along the hillside, to reduce soil wash. In the plains one sees strips ploughed athwart the wind to reduce the risk of "blowing".

An agricultural pattern has emerged, adjusted to the physical influences of terrain, soil, and climate, and to the economic factors of labour, transport, market and price. The regions shown in fig. 25 vary somewhat with market conditions, but this marginal fluctuation is not enough to influence their general stability. This agricultural pattern is described in detail in the chapters which follow.

The agricultural production of the continent has mounted steadily. In the last sixty years the numbers of farm stock and the volume of wheat production have doubled, and the output of other farm products increased sharply. The increase in the production of citrus and other fruits has been the most marked; this has occurred in the present century, chiefly since the first World War, with the increasing use of irrigation. Production, at least in the staple products of farm and ranch, may not increase greatly above the present level, because the climatic margin of profitable cultivation has in many areas been reached. The lesson of the thirties has been well enough learned for Americans not to tempt nature by taking too great a liberty with their cultivation of marginal areas. Only two frontiers remain for further expansion of agriculture: the dry frontier to the West and the cold frontier of the North. Each will be described in later chapters.

THE MINERAL WEALTH OF THE CONTINENT. It is in its mineral resources that the great endowment of North America appears most conspicuous. Coal, petroleum and iron resources are large, and there are abundant reserves of almost all significant non-ferrous minerals with the exception of tin.

This endowment is probably richest in coal. Three coal-fields, each of great extent and enormous wealth lie across the continent. The earliest to be developed was the Appalachian. Beginning in the mountains of north-western Pennsylvania, the field stretches south-westwards into northern Alabama (see fig. 10). Production is greatest and reserves

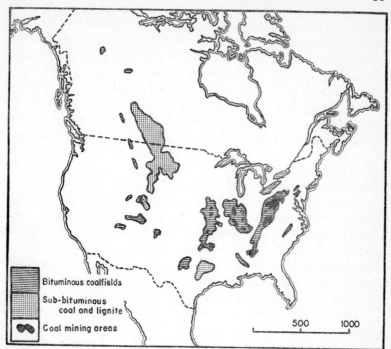

Fig. 10. THE COALFIELDS OF NORTH AMERICA

largest in Pennsylvania, West Virginia and Kentucky (see pp. 89–91).
All important varieties of coal are mined; seams are thick; folding and
faulting are slight, and the extraction easy and economical. Furthermore this coal-field lies close to the most densely populated and highly
industrialized area of the continent. These are very good reasons why
it is the most important field not only in the continent, but also in the
whole world. Geologically distinct from though closely related to the
Appalachian field are the small anthracite coal-field of eastern Pennsylvania (fig. 10 and p. 89) and the small and unimportant fields in
Virginia and North Carolina.

A more significant outlier of the Appalachian coal-field is that of
Nova Scotia in Canada. The most important workings are on Cape
Breton Island, lying close to the coast and permitting of easy and cheap
transport by sea.

Second in importance to the Appalachian field is the eastern Interior
field. This extends over a large part of the State of Illinois and parts of
neighbouring Indiana and Kentucky. Coal lies in thick, almost level

D

seams. Most of it has a high proportion of volatile constituents. It burns with a great deal of smoke and its industrial uses are limited. Very little of it, for example, is suited for the metallurgical industries of the Chicago area. On the other hand, it is mined relatively cheaply, and a great deal of it is stripped by means of giant machines in shallow open pits.

The Western Interior Field is no less extensive than the eastern, but its development has made less progress, because demand has been small in the western plains and the quality of the coal is itself inferior to that mined in the Appalachian fields. There is a number of scattered fields of bituminous coal in the Rocky Mountain states, and these are continued northwards into the Prairies and Rocky Mountains of Canada. Though the reserves appear to be very large, the quality of coal is not in general adequate for many modern needs. In the Canadian Province of British Columbia, however, are small deposits of high quality coal, which are worked on Vancouver Island and in a few places in the Rocky Mountain chain. In North Dakota and Montana, in neighbouring Saskatchewan, as well as in Texas are large deposits of lignite or brown coal. Though these are worked and the coal is burned locally, the deposits are of very small importance to the continent as a whole.

The mining of bituminous coal has mounted very rapidly in the last half century, increasing in the United States roughly tenfold in some sixty years. It has, however, constituted a diminishing proportion of the total energy consumption throughout this period, as the consumption of the cleaner and more convenient fuels, petroleum and natural gas, has increased.

The petroleum and natural gas industries are the creation of the present century. Though the first productive well was drilled as far back as 1859, at Titusville, Pennsylvania, there was no sharp increase in output until the end of the century. At first the production was chiefly from the eastern states, but after 1906, the mid-continent field of Texas, Oklahoma, Arkansas and Kansas was developed. The boom in the South Californian industry came in the 1920's, the development of the Gulf field of southern Texas in the 1930's. The oil-fields of Mexico lying inland from Tampico, on the Gulf coast, are in a sense a continuation of those of southern Texas. The Mexican field was discovered at the beginning of the present century. The peak of Mexican production was achieved soon after the first World War, and since then production has slowly declined with the exhaustion of the known fields.

The development of the petroleum resources of Canada has been more recent. Lack of transport facilities and the inadequacy of geological surveys have held it up. There appear to be deposits along the eastern foothills of the Canadian Rockies from the American border northwards into the Mackenzie Valley. Hitherto the most vigorous developments have been in the Turner Valley field, near Calgary in Alberta, but the construction in recent years of roads into the far north has revealed the existence of other and possibly very large oil-fields. New "strikes" of oil are of almost daily occurrence in Alberta, and Canada is advancing rapidly to the position of one of the larger producers of crude oil.

Closely related to the petroleum is the natural gas industry. Gas from the oil wells was formerly allowed to burn off. It is now stored and distributed by a network of pipe lines very much larger and more complex than that constructed for the transmission of oil. The natural gas pipe lines of the United States exceed in length the total mileage of railroad.

Pipe lines, for both petroleum and natural gas, have been laid down between the chief producing centres and both the ports of California and the Gulf coast, and the important producing centres in the east.

North America appears to have adequate reserves of the mineral fuels for a very long period, but the resources in iron ore are very much smaller. By far the largest production—about 90 per cent of the United States total—has come from the deposits that lie around the head of Lake Superior, in the States of Michigan, Wisconsin and Minnesota. This ore is a fairly high grade haematite, much of it easily mined from large open cuts and despatched conveniently by iron-ore freighters on the Great Lakes. The greater part of the iron-smelting industry of the continent is supplied from this ore-field, but the reserves are limited and the end of the higher grade ore is said to be in sight. There ate, however, very large deposits of a lower grade ore, known as taconire, and at present attempts are being made to "beneficiate" this ore—that is, to increase its metal content, thus diminishing the transport costs. At the same time, newly discovered deposits of ore, deep in the interior of the Laurentian Shield, in Labrador, are being opened up. A railway has been built from the St. Lawrence estuary to the deposits, and if the St. Lawrence "seaway" is completed it is highly probable that these ores will come gradually to replace those now obtained from the upper Great Lakes.

The only other deposit of great significance is that in northern Alabama, which supplies the smelting industry of Birmingham. Other, though less significant, deposits are worked on Bell Island off northern

Newfoundland, in the Appalachians of New Jersey and New York, in the more southerly parts of the Laurentian Shield and in some of the western states.

Deposits of ores of the non-ferrous metals are large. The Rocky Mountain states are richly endowed with copper deposits. These are mostly low grade, but are extracted and processed by exceptionally heavy equipment and are made to yield a very large quantity of metal-

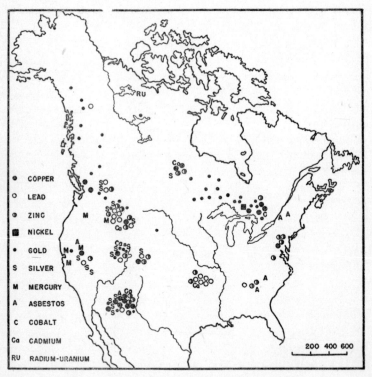

Fig. 11. THE MINING OF NON-FERROUS METALS

lic copper. Arizona and Utah are the chief sources. Lead and zinc are produced in quantity in the so-called Tri-State district, where Missouri, Kansas and Oklahoma meet, and in the northern Rockies and Canadian Shield. Almost the whole of the continent's large production of nickel is from the Sudbury district of Ontario. Mercury is obtained from the mountains of California, Oregon and Idaho. Gold occurs widely in the Rocky Mountain system and in the Canadian Shield, and silver is associated with most of the deposits of lead and zinc. Uranium is found in the older rocks of parts of the Shield. Some minerals occur, however, in quantities that are quite inadequate to meet the needs of the two nations that share the continent. Tin occurs in only an infinitesimal quantity. There are, on balance, small imports of cobalt, tungsten and mercury, and large imports of manganese and tin.

The map, fig. 11, shows a number of marked areas of concentration of the non-ferrous metals. Arizona and Idaho are outstanding; then come Utah and Colorado, the Tri-State district and the Canadian Rockies and Canadian Shield. There is a smaller production from the Appalachians, and almost none from the Great Plains.

It is unlikely that any major deposits of the non-ferrous metals remain to be discovered in the United States, but so little is known of the geological structure of northern Canada that there may be very large undiscovered reserves. The nature of the rocks that make up this area strongly favours this supposition.

In other minerals also the continent is well endowed; the sulphur of Louisiana, the phosphate rock of Florida, Tennessee and the northern mountain states; the salt deposits of the Gulf coast and of the Great Lakes states; the potash salts of New Mexico, Utah and California; the immense supply of building stone and abrasives, of clay for pottery and cement; the free-cutting limestone of Indiana; the granite and marble of New England and an abundance of coarse, hard stone for road beds and concrete. All this adds up to an immense endowment. In very few naturally occurring resources would the continent be dependent, in an emergency, on outside sources.

POPULATION. The most recent censuses give the population of the continent as:

Canada (1951)	14,009,429
Continental United States (1950)	152,302,361
Alaska (1950)	128,643

The graph, fig. 12, shows how rapidly this population has increased. The population of the continent before the arrival of the white man was probably not more than two millions. The rest have immigrated, most from Europe, some from Mexico, China and Japan, and a considerable proportion involuntarily from Africa. The population of the United States contained in 1950, 15,042,286 coloured, i.e. negroes, and 713,047 other non-whites. The negro population remains heavily concentrated in the South (see pp. 118–19) and the oriental along the Pacific coast. Mexicans are numerous in the border states from California to Texas, but they also travel widely in the United States in search of agricultural work.

Both Canada and the United States have been faced almost since their creation with the problem of assimilating large bodies of immigrants, foreign in language and traditions, to their own evolving way of life. The process is very far indeed from complete, and every day fresh groups of immigrants arrive, displaced persons, refugees, those forced from their original homes by economic pressure and those attracted by the economic advantages of the new continent. Some immigrant groups tend to form small, compact communities in which they

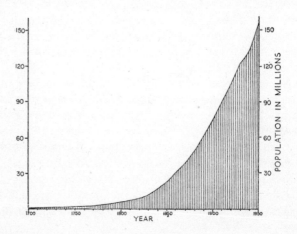

Fig. 12. GROWTH OF POPULATION IN THE UNITED STATES

speak their language and preserve their traditions. Sections of the great cities (see fig. 28) are often given over to such communities. Even in the rural areas they form distinct and homogeneous groups: the Finns of Michigan, the Swedes of Minnesota, the Germans of Wisconsin.

Some of these groups are sufficiently large, homogeneous and powerful to exercise a strong though not always enlightened influence on the internal and foreign policy of both the United States and Canada. The "hyphenated" groups—the Irish-Americans, Italian-Americans, Jewish-Americans, Polish-Americans and many others are very articulate, and unfortunately they often carry over to their new homes the ambitions, fears and jealousies which had characterized their original homelands. In Canada the French-speaking Canadians constitute such a group of exceptional size and significance, with, however, this difference, that the French-speaking population was established here before the arrival of the English-speaking and, far from becoming assimilated to the English majority, would be more likely to assimilate the latter to it (see pp. 168–70). This acute fractionalization of the population of the United States and Canada presents obstacles to the development of national unity. In time of crisis both are liable to speak with many—and conflicting—voices.

On the other hand, this large population permits the development of manufacturing industries and transport services on a scale that is not met with in the old world. A market as large as that of the United States, with as high a purchasing power as it possesses, is the pre-requisite for the growth of a manufacturing unit of the size of General Motors, the United States Steel Company or the International Har-vester Company. Cheapness of production is, in part at least, a function of the size of the undertaking. It cannot be emphasized too strongly that the United States offers to the manufacturer a market larger than that provided by the whole of western Europe, and one, moreover, that is without customs barriers and almost completely devoid of barriers to internal trade.[1]

The great majority of factory workers in the U.S.A. live and work in the area to the east of the Mississippi and north of the Ohio. This region has considerable advantages not only in the resources which it embraces, but also in the historical development and the economic momentum of the area. It was in the north-east of the country that the earliest manufacturing industries were established. Iron ore from the coastal bogs was smelted with charcoal from the neighbouring forests. The streams descending from the hills were made to drive the small, early woollen mills, and power the tanneries, saw mills and furni-ture works. Manufacturing industries were slow to move westwards with the expansion of settlement. The frontier was supplied from the rear areas. It was late in the nineteenth century before the quest for coal fuel, and the rapidly expanding western frontier of settlement, took industry across the Appalachians. The textile industry remained in New England; the iron and steel industry spread into the valleys of the headwaters of the Ohio River.

The function of Detroit and later of Chicago as the starting point of western routes quickly gave them an industrial importance. A close net-work of railways between Chicago in the west and Boston in the east, facilitated the movement of raw materials and finished goods. Within this region the concentration of population offered a large market with

[1] That some such barriers do exist is shown, however, by the prohibition of the import of fruit and vegetables into California.

only a short haul from the factories. In the words of an American geographer "an axis of maximum market potential . . . runs through the heart of the manufacturing belt extending from New York City on the east to Chicago on the west. It passes through Philadelphia, Baltimore, Pittsburgh, Cleveland and Detroit. . . ."[1]

In the last half-century this industrial concentration has continued to expand, into Michigan, Wisconsin and Illinois, and at the same time to become more dense within its earlier limits. Across the plains of Ohio, Indiana and southern Michigan, small towns developed engineering, electronic, furniture and many other industries.

One region within the north-eastern industrial region has shown a sharp decline. The textile industry of New England owed its position to the impetus of its early establishment. It was remote from mineral fuels and from its own raw materials. During the present century New England has been to a considerable extent replaced in the textile industry by the South.

There is a thin, irregular scattering of manufacturing industries in other parts of the United States. A belt of industrial centres stretches from Virginia to Alabama. In the main, these are concerned with cotton textiles, but synthetic fibres and chemicals are becoming important. An even thinner scatter is found from Texas northwards to Kansas and there are a few small industrial centres in Colorado. But the most marked increase of manufacturing industry, outside the north-east, has taken place along the Pacific coast. The Puget Sound and Portland areas in the north, and further south, San Francisco and Los Angeles have each become the scene of a very varied as well as vigorous industrial growth. This expansion has accompanied the increase of population on the Pacific coast states and also the growing importance of the Orient in the commerce and strategy of the United States.

Industrial development in Canada has been slower than in the United States, and, even relative to its much smaller population, it remains small. Canada lacks certain of the natural advantages of the United States—the production of sub-tropical crops such as cotton, and an abundance of easily accessible coal and iron. It has on the other hand, immense reserves of hydro-electric power, and the utilization of this source of energy is leading, at the present time, to a very intensive and rapid industrialization. This industrial development is taking place largely in the St. Lawrence Valley and the Lakes Peninsula of Ontario, and in British Columbia.

[1] Chauncy D. Harris, in *Annals of the Association of American Geographers* XLIII, 1953, p. 172.

An immense variety of industries is engaged in the production of what are termed consumers' goods, articles that are usually marketed in the shops, are bought, used up and replaced. The largest market for such goods is in the greater centres of population, and the manufacturing units usually tend to be close to these centres. But the manufacture of some consumers' goods and of some more durable goods has a distribution pattern that does not conform with that of population.

The manufacture of textiles, originally located in New England, has spread to the South during the present century, as the advantages of New England dimished. There is very little textile production in Canada. The location of the iron and steel industry, like that of the cotton textiles, is much influenced by the desire to be as close as possible to its raw materials. The late nineteenth-century centres of iron smelting and steel making were located in the northern Appalachians, where there was a supply both of iron ore and of coking coal (see p. 92). It next spread to the shores of the Great Lakes, where the neighbourhood of Chicago became a centre of production of outstanding importance. The new sites were so chosen as to be able to import their iron ore from the Upper Great Lakes by steamer and also to receive their fuel from the Appalachian field. The rise of a large market on the Pacific coast has led to the establishment of a number of steel works in the West. Steel making is more widely distributed than iron smelting. The latter is concentrated in the Pittsburgh and Chicago and Great Lakes areas. These supply pig iron to the scattered steel works.

An important change is now taking place in the pattern of iron smelting. The approaching exhaustion of the great deposits around the shores of Lake Superior has led to an increasing interest in the iron ores of the West Indies and of Central and South America. These ores, imported by sea, are most conveniently smelted on the Atlantic coast. Works have been established at Baltimore (Sparrow's Point), and at Philadelphia to handle the ores. New blast-furnace and steel works are being erected at Philadelphia and Bridgeport (Conn.). The opening up of the Labrador iron ores, especially if it is supplemented by the completion of the St. Lawrence seaway, may remove the threat, created by a possible shortage of ore, to the Pittsburgh-Chicago region.

TRANSPORT. So widespread an industrial pattern, serving the needs of a continent, is clearly dependent upon a very highly organized transport system. By far the largest proportion of the freight is moved by rail. Road transport is important, but river and canal are relatively unimportant. The United States has about a quarter of a million miles of railway, roughly a third of the world's total. Canada has approximately 42,956 miles. There are no fewer than 43 railway companies in the United States and 2 in Canada, each operating more than 1,000 miles of main line track. Except in Canada, where each of the two main companies—the Canadian Pacific and the Canadian National—operates lines which run from the Atlantic to the Pacific coasts, there are no systems which span the continent. The more important are either "eastern lines", with New York and Chicago as their major termini, or they are "western lines", running from Chicago or St. Louis across the prairies and mountains. While a journey across the continent can be made in the United States without changing railway coaches, it is usual to change in Chicago not merely from an eastern to a western line, but from one railway station to another. This awkward and often irritating circumstance derives from the early history of transport and from the former role of Chicago as the starting point for travellers to the West. It means that to-day Chicago is a railway centre of unparalleled importance. The city is served by 22 major railroads and 16 minor, and is said to contain no less than 7,800 miles of track and 206 freight yards.

Most of the main lines run from east to west, from the Atlantic and Pacific coast ports into their hinterlands. Except along the coasts and in the Mississippi Valley there is a notable lack of north-south lines. The continent is clearly "stratified" in an east-west direction, and the need for north-south communications is not strongly felt.

Although in the nineteenth century there was something of a canal "mania" and a number of canals were cut, these retain in general no more significance than they do in England. With a very few exceptions, water-borne transport plays an unimportant role in North America. These exceptions are, first and foremost, the St. Lawrence River and Great Lakes. Below Montreal and above the Niagara Falls there is no serious obstacle to navigation. A large canal, the Welland Canal, circumvents the Niagara Falls, but short lengths of canal which were cut to avoid the rapids on the river between Lake Ontario and Montreal are inadequate for modern needs. It is the extension of these that constitutes the St. Lawrence seaway project (see p. 180).

The Mississippi River also constitutes an exception, though it is not by any means used to capacity. To some extent the deliberate and ruthless competition of the railway companies has reduced its importance, but it owes its relative unimportance rather to the fact that it flows across the general direction of traffic movement. The river and canal connection between the Mississippi and Chicago is used, as is also the

New York State Barge Canal, which supplements the Mohawk River and links it with Erie. A few of the southern rivers bear a small traffic but this has no great significance.

Road transport is, relative to Europe, very important. The excellence of the road system, the cheapness of motor fuel and the flexibility in use of the "truck" have combined to make road transport a serious rival of rail. Its importance is enhanced by the great size of the trucks normally used.

NATIONAL INCOME. The total value of the products and services of the continent within a period of a year is measured by means of its national income.[1] If we take the national income of each country in the world and divide it by the number of people in it, we arrive at a rough measure of the value of all goods made and services performed by the average individual. We thus have a means of comparing the average incomes of individuals in the various countries and thus, if only approximately, their standards of living. On this basis, the highest standards in the world are met with in the United States, and the second highest in Canada.

The immensely high national incomes of the United States and Canada do not imply that there is no poverty in these countries. The range of real income, from the wealthiest to the poorest, is very much greater—even several times as great—as it is in England. A policy of "redistributing" wealth, such as has been practised in England by means of steeply graduated tax rates, subsidized foodstuffs, family allowances and "nationalized" medicine, has so far not been seriously practised in North America. In consequence the contrast between the ostentatious wealth in certain suburbs of the great cities and the poverty of the Tennessee mountaineer, the southern "cropper" or the Chicago tenement is something which the Old World can only rarely show.

This enormous productivity, reflected in the high national incomes, is the result of many factors. Amongst these is the access which both Americans and Canadians have had in recent years to large and virgin natural resources and also their access to an immense, duty-free market at home. Further, in the development of these resources, the inhabitants of the New World were spared the long and costly period of experimentation which was necessary in Europe. Granted that the Americans have further developed and enlarged the inventions of the Old World, and that they have perfected the technique of mass-production, they

[1] These terms are defined in the volume in this series devoted to Economic Geography.

were nevertheless able to take over from Europe, in a working if not perfect condition, the railway locomotive, the modern methods of producing iron and steel and the great inventions made by the English in the production of textiles. They also took over European agricultural methods and adapted them to the conditions of the New World.

But this does not wholly explain the immense productivity of the continent. It has been accompanied by a readiness to accept risks and to make experiments such as had not in recent years been conspicuous in the productive activities of the Old World. The replacement of hand labour by machines has gone very much further and American machines are generally larger and, especially in terms of the labour involved in using them, more efficient than the European.

This contrast between equipment and management in Great Britain and in the United States has been emphasized by the reports of technical missions sent to examine American conditions. The reports of the Cotton Textile Mission of 1944 and of a delegation of the British Iron and Steel Industry of 1951 underline these conditions. A paragraph from the latter summarizes the position:

> The material standard of living of America is probably twice as high as that of any European country. This is reflected in a correspondingly high consumption of steel, to which consumption the development of public and private transport, of skyscrapers and of the mechanised kitchen have all contributed. This high standard of living is partly the outcome of historical forces and of the character of the American people; but its indispensable foundation was the country's exceptional natural resources.
>
> Geographical concentration by district is matched by a concentration of output in large works, encouraged by the great distances involved, which made necessary a substantial investment in large-scale transport. The perennial shortage of labour in relation to resources encouraged mechanisation; the market is very large and highly standardised; and intensive competition has stimulated both the amalgamation of firms and investment in sources of raw materials.
>
> Finally, a high proportion of the American industry is of recent construction, thanks not only to the rapid expansion of the population and the economy, but also to Government investment and tax concessions for defence purposes.[1]

[1] Productivity Team Report, *Iron and Steel* (H.M.S.O., 1952).

— 4 —

New York City

IN 1609 Henry Hudson, sailing west along the coast of New England, came to the head of a shallow bay, from which a navigable waterway led northwards. He followed it between its high cliffs, convinced that it was the long sought North-West Passage, leading to the Pacific Ocean. He was disillusioned and turned back when the broad waterway narrowed and showed unmistakably that it was a river. But those features which had suggested so strongly to him that this must be a water route through the continent nevertheless recommended it as the site of a settlement and port. In 1624 the Dutch, in whose service he had sailed, established their first settlement on the banks of the Hudson River, and two years later they founded New Amsterdam. In 1664 the name was altered, after its capture by the British, to New York.

SITE AND SITUATION. The site of New York combines two incalculable advantages. It lies at the seaward end of the easiest crossing of the Appalachian Mountains, and it has one of the most perfect natural harbours in the world.

The ridges of the Appalachians have been truncated in the longitude of New York by the southward flowing Hudson River. For a distance of some 200 miles it occupies a valley sometimes wide, but more often narrow, and always sharply bounded by the high walls of the Taconic Mountains of New England on the east and the Adirondack and Catskill Mountains to the west. Between these last two masses is the valley of the eastward flowing Mohawk, which joins the Hudson 140 miles above New York. The Mohawk Valley is, in reality, a glacial overflow (see p. 85) by which the meltwater from the ice sheet, which during the Pleistocene period covered the region of the Great Lakes, reached the sea. Its broad, flat valley was in parts marshy, but it offered a routeway generally flat and nowhere rising as much as 500 feet above sealevel.

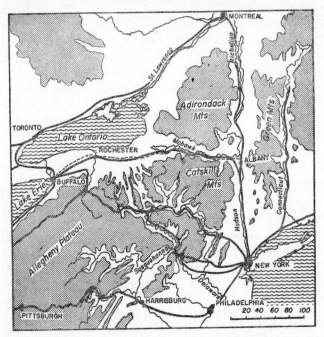

Fig. 13. NEW YORK: ITS REGIONAL SETTING

We have already seen (p. 10) how the Iroquois federation restricted the usefulness of this route, so that it was not until late in the eighteenth century that it was much used as a routeway to the Mid-West. But when once the barrier of hostile Indians was removed its development was rapid. Its almost level nature recommended it for canal development. In 1821 part of a canal to link the Hudson to Lake Erie was opened. In 1825 the canal was complete, and the agricultural produce of Ohio and Indiana began to move towards the port of New York. New York's hinterland was extended to include much of the Mid-West, and New York found herself in competition with New Orleans for the traffic of the Ohio Valley.

The Erie Canal was later rebuilt as the New York State Barge Canal, linking the Hudson with the Lake Erie port of Buffalo. It still carries a large volume of traffic, though for the whole of its length it is paralleled by at least two railways.

The second advantage possessed by New York is the excellence of its harbour. The coast has been subject to a positive movement of sea level in geologically recent times. This has resulted in the submergence of coastal areas and the production of many islands and deep bays.

Their shapes have subsequently been smoothed and rounded by the longshore movement of beach material. Largest of the islands is Long Island, which stretches 120 miles from the mouth of the Hudson to its most easterly extremity. Between it and the shore of New England is Long Island Sound, a shallow waterway of varying width. Between the most westerly point of Long Island and the Hudson River is Manhattan, and, south of the latter, Staten Island and a number of smaller islets.

The Lower Bay of New York harbour lies between Long Island, Staten Island and the shore of New Jersey (fig. 14), partially protected by Sandy Hook on the south and Rockaway Beach on the north. The Lower Bay thus has some degree of protection from the ocean, but the Upper Bay, which communicates with the Lower by The Narrows, is almost entirely land-locked. To the north is the broad, deep Hudson River; to the north-east, the winding East River which expands into Long Island Sound; to the west, the narrow opening of Kill van Kull communicates with Newark Bay and with Arthur Kill, which cuts off Staten Island from the mainland. There can be few harbours in the world with so great a length of sheltered and protected shoreline where large vessels may tie up. The total water-frontage in New York City is 578 miles and there are jetties and quays along almost the whole of it.

The tidal rise and fall averages only four feet, making the construction of tidal basins and reliance upon the tide to bring vessels in and out unnecessary. The largest liners are able to sail up the Hudson and tie up at their berth at any stage of the tide. In these respects the port of New York compares very favourably with those of London and Southampton.

The original settlement of New York was established on the southern tip of Manhattan Island, where the fort and early warehouses of the Dutch were built. Manhattan is in general about two miles across from west to east and almost thirteen miles long from its northern to its southern extremities. The city expanded gradually northwards and to-day the whole island, with the exception of its parks, is built up. Very early in its development, settlers spilled over to east and west. Beyond the East River Brooklyn (from the Dutch *Breuckelen*) was settled by the Dutch; beyond the Hudson, Hoboken and Weehawken. To-day New York City, comprising the boroughs of Manhattan, Richmond, Brooklyn, Queens and Bronx, spans Staten Island, the western extremity of Long Island and part of the mainland, north of the Harlem River, which joins the Hudson with Long Island Sound, in addition to Manhattan itself. It has a land area of 279 square miles and a popula-

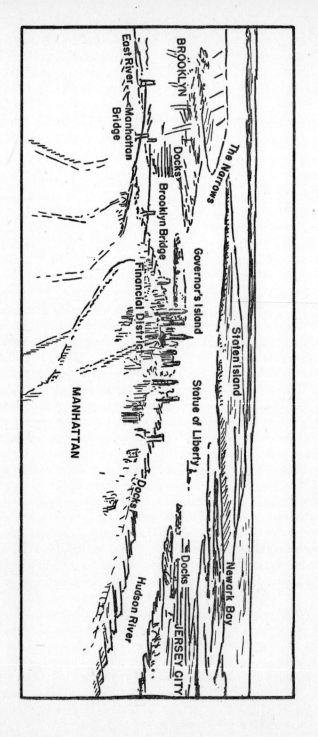

NEW YORK CITY, *looking southwards over Manhattan to the Atlantic Ocean.*

The Narrows

Staten Island

Newark Bay

BROOKLYN

East River

Manhattan Bridge

Docks

Brooklyn Bridge

Governor's Island

Financial District

Statue of Liberty

MANHATTAN

Docks

Docks

Hudson River

JERSEY CITY

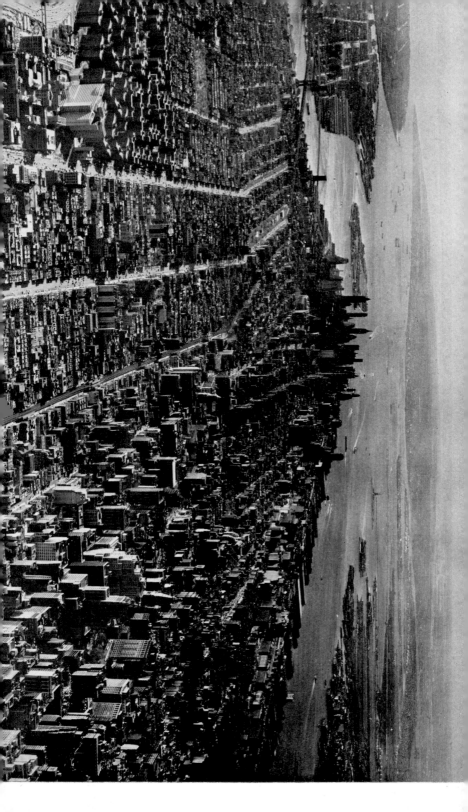

NEW YORK CITY, *looking northwards up the Hudson River.*

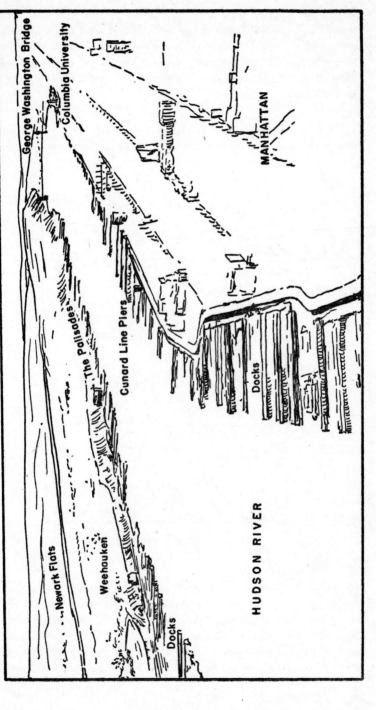

George Washington Bridge

Columbia University

MANHATTAN

The Palisades

Cunard Line Piers

Docks

Newark Flats

Weehauken

Docks

HUDSON RIVER

E

tion of 7,455,000. But contiguous with New York City, and with difficulty distinguishable from it, is Metropolitan New York, a vast conurba-
tion which stretches westwards beyond the Hudson to include Jersey
City, Bayonne, Newark and Elizabeth, and northwards up the river
to Yonkers.

NEW YORK CITY. New York is not only one of the largest but also
one of the most varied and beautiful cities in the world. Manhattan,

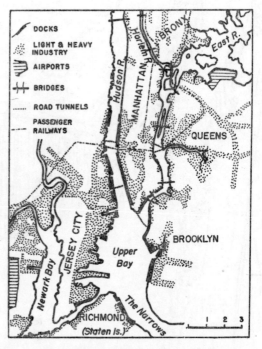

Fig. 14. THE SITE OF NEW YORK

on which lies its core, is a tabular mass of old, hard rocks, which rises
to the north, and forms picturesque cliffs which look across the Hudson
to the even steeper cliffs, or "palisades" formed by a basaltic intrusion.
No part of the city is much more than a mile from the water, and from
most of the tall buildings it is possible to look out over the busy movement of liners, cargo vessels, tugs and ferry boats. But if New York

owes part of its atmosphere to its rivers and bays, it owes far more to its tall buildings.

Geographers have given very good reasons for the skyscraper architecture of New York City. They point to the confined space on Manhattan and the consequent need to expand vertically, and to the hard, palaeozoic rock which forms a firm foundation. No reasoning could be further from the truth. The skyscraper was born, not on the hard rock of Manhattan but in the marshes of Chicago, where the first skyscraper was built in 1883–4. It was not until the end of the century that New York had a building any taller. But from that time the fashion spread. Possession of a tall building conferred prestige on the commercial house that used it. The erection of some has been popularly attributed to the rivalries between companies. But their erection has never been motivated by reasons of economy. The taller the building becomes, the greater is the cost of adding a single storey. It is still profitable to erect buildings of three or four storeys, and most of the built-up area of New York City is covered with buildings whose average height is no greater than those of London.

The tall buildings of New York divide into two groups. The older lies at the southern tip of Manhattan, site of the early Dutch settlement and later the financial and business hub of the United States. Here, in the years before the First World War, a group of skyscrapers was built, each rising directly from the street and all so closely massed that the sky scarcely appears between them. The streets, narrow in any case, are overshadowed by them, so that they seem to be always in a kind of half-light. When during the 1920's a fresh group of skyscrapers was built they were located on the expanding northern fringe of the city. City building regulations prevented a building from rising directly from the street for all its forty or fifty storeys, requiring instead that at certain heights the vertical line should be set back. A result is that the more recent buildings have a pyramidal shape and are more widely spaced. The Empire State Building, the tallest in the world, was completed in the 1920s. The erection of tall buildings ceased during the depression of the thirties, and the United Nations Building is the only important example built since that time.

The city of New York, like almost every other great city, is divided into "quarters", each the traditional seat of some occupation or the home of a particular community. Amid the tall buildings of southern Manhattan is the financial and business quarter, gathered round the Stock Exchange in Wall Street. Along Lower East Side is the Chinatown, and to the west of it Greenwich Village, the *quartier latin* of New

York. North of this, near Thirty-fifth Street[1] is the important clothing industry. Beyond Forty-second Street is the "theatreland" and the luxury shopping district of Fifth Avenue. In the midst of the island is the oblong Central Park; to the west, a high quality residential area overlooks the Hudson and contains Columbia University; to the east are poor tenement blocks and the run-down quarters inhabited by certain immigrant groups. To the north of the Central Park and running down to the East River, is the negro quarter of Harlem.

West of Manhattan, in Jersey City and Bayonne, and over the marshy flats of Newark and Elizabeth are a variety of industries: oil refining, soap and paint manufacture, engineering, chemical manufacture and the smelting of non-ferrous metals. Factories line the shore of Newark Bay and Kill van Kull and stretch northwards along the Passaic River.

Residential areas lie in all directions from Manhattan. Brooklyn, Queens and Bronx are chiefly residential. The morning "commuters' " trains bring workers into New York City from far out on Long Island, from Connecticut, from far up the Hudson Valley and from hundreds of little towns west of the river in New Jersey and New York State.

TRANSPORT. The waterways, which serve New York so well in her overseas commerce, are a grave hindrance to the internal movement of New York City. Manhattan is an island, and all the surrounding waterways, except the Harlem River in the north, are wide and deep. From the earliest days a heavy reliance has been placed on ferries, and the ferries are still an important and, in good weather, one of the most pleasant means of reaching the outlying parts of the metropolitan area.

The main railways approach New York either by tunnelling under the Hudson River (the *Pennsylvania R.R.*) or by following the Hudson Valley and crossing the narrow Harlem River on to Manhattan (the *New York Central* and *New York, New Haven and Hartford R.R's.*). Others have their termini on the west bank of the Hudson and are linked with Manhattan by ferry.

The development of motor transport has raised a further problem: the paucity of bridges and the high cost of their construction. There are now five large bridges joining Manhattan with Long Island, but still only one, the George Washington Bridge, across the Hudson. Several bridges, including the triangular Triborough Bridge, link Manhattan with the mainland to the north. In addition to the bridges, there are two tunnels (each resembling very closely the Mersey Tunnel in

---

[1] The numbered "streets" run from west to east across Manhattan. The numbering begins at the south of Manhattan. The north-south thoroughfares are known as "Avenues"; most of these are numbered.

England) under the Hudson and two under the East River. Altogether there are fifty-eight bridges with spans varying in length from 65 to 3,500 feet.

In order to assist the movement of traffic into and out of New York, numerous "parkways" and super-highways have been built. They encircle Manhattan and Brooklyn and reach out along each side of Long Island Sound and up the Hudson Valley. Traffic is very fast on these roads; stops are not permitted and the few junctions are of the "clover-leaf" design which obviates the need for one stream of traffic to cross another. Super-highways have been built through the industrial area of Newark, where the roads are raised on viaducts and bridges high above the factories, houses and winding creeks of the Passaic River. No one who has seen the congestion of traffic on these roads can doubt either their necessity or their inadequacy.

The air age has introduced a further complexity into the geography of New York's transport. An airfield, the La Guardia Airport, was laid out on the southern shore of the East River, within seven miles of the centre of Manhattan. This has proved to be inadequate, and is used now chiefly for internal flights. A newer airfield has been laid out at Idlewild, five miles further to the east, on Long Island, for international air traffic.

TRADE AND INDUSTRY. New York is incomparably the greatest port in the New World, and handles no less than about 50 per cent by value of the foreign commerce of the United States in addition to a very heavy coastwise traffic. It has "a waterfront of about 770 miles with a developed frontage measured around piers and ships of nearly 550 miles".[1] Most of the larger vessels tie up at piers built forward into the Hudson along Manhattan shore. The task of getting freight to the loading piers (where there is no railway) is sometimes awkward and always expensive. Such bulk commodities as petroleum, coal, ores and timber are unloaded either on the New Jersey shore or in Brooklyn, where there is the advantage of railway transport at the dock.

The difficulties of transport limit the industries of much of New York to the lighter ones in which a relatively small volume of materials is used. The huge population of the New York area creates a market for consumers' goods. Most important of New York's manufactures is clothing. Half the American clothing industry is carried on in small and unpretentious factories in the lower west side of Manhattan. In addi-

[1] *The Port of New York*, Port Series No. 20, U.S. Army (Corps of Engineers), (Washington D.C., 1932), p. 1.

tion, printing and publishing, both of books and of newspapers and periodicals, and food processing are important. Add to these the fact that lower Manhattan contains the chief financial centre in America: the stock and commodity exchanges, the leading banks and the offices of the chief shipping companies. With the growing importance of the dollar in recent years has come the increasing importance of Wall Street which, from having once been the financial quarter of a large city, has grown to be the nation's and now the world's business and banking centre.

New York: A Social Problem. Many of New York's problems are geographical. The assets—such as the many rivers which gave protection and encouraged commerce—have been turned into disadvantages which it costs billions of dollars to overcome. The water supply of the great city has to be drawn from the mountains on both sides of the Hudson Valley. Almost the whole of the Catskill Mountains constitutes a water catchment area for New York. But New York has a further problem which derives chiefly from the fact that it has been for a century the chief port of entry into the United States. It has a vast, unassimilated population. It is, for example, unusual to hear English spoken on some of the streets; Italian is much more common. The immigrant, if he stayed in New York, gravitated toward the quarter where his fellow-countrymen lived. There, in conditions that sometimes amounted almost to social ostracism, the worst qualities of the immigrant groups were emphasized. The "underworld" of the gangsters, predominantly an Italian-run business, had, and probably retains still, close ties with similar extra-legal organizations in Italy.

Many immigrants, especially those from eastern and southern Europe, came expecting greater comfort and security in the New World than they had ever known in the Old. Many were sadly disappointed, and the disappointment of their hopes has led to bitterness and sometimes revolt. The population of New York, taken by and large, is not one of the more law-abiding.

It is strange that the richest country in the world should contain some of the poorest, most depressed living quarters. The slums along part of Manhattan's east side, where East European and coloured peoples live, would be a disgrace to the city (and the same is true of Chicago, St. Louis and many of the other great cities) if the circumstances which created them were not understood. Much has been done in recent years to clear the tenement blocks and to build modern flats. In contrast with this squalor is the glamour, luxury and sophistication of Fifth Avenue, centre of fashion, and of expensive hotels, such as the Waldorf.

From this gateway to the continent, we shall in the following chapters explore first New England, lying to the north-east; then the Atlantic seaboard and the Appalachians, lying to the south; then the Mid-West, the South, the West, the Far West and Canada.

— 5 —

New England

NEW ENGLAND is the region lying to the east of the Hudson River and to the north-east of New York City. On its northern boundary lies Canada, and to the south and east is the sea. It is, apart from New York City, the smallest of the units into which, for the purposes of this book, the continent of North America is divided. It is, we have already seen (p. 22), a hilly region, with a coastal plain bordering the ocean and mountains in the north and west. It is one of the most distinctive parts of the United States. New England is a palimpsest of American life, in which can be discerned, superimposed one on the other, the various strata that have gone to make up the American people. Each period in its history, each generation of its immigrants has left some kind of imprint on the landscape and in the culture of New England. The twisting, narrow Boston streets, that could so easily belong to an older European city; the Wren-style churches, imitated in New England wood and brick; the Georgian-style mansions; the numerous and, by American standards ancient, universities and colleges; all these combine to make New England appear more English—or, at least, more European—than any other part of the continent except perhaps parts of French-speaking Canada.

The earliest European settlers in New England were the Pilgrim Fathers, followed by the high-minded and quarrelsome members of the Massachusetts Bay Company. They settled around the shores of Massachusetts Bay, laid out their farms and established the industries in wood, cloth and leather that still remain. The place-names: Worcester, Haverhill, Braintree, Cambridge and Boston, speak of Old England, and East Anglia in particular, whence a large part of the Puritan settlers had come. Groups of people, seeking either more virgin land to till or freedom from the religious intolerance that characterized Massachusetts society, spread southwards to Rhode Island, westwards into the Connecticut Valley or northwards, up the Merrimac Valley, into New Hampshire. The more hardy of them settled in the mountains of Vermont or the forests of Maine.

At the time of the declaration of American independence there were five states in New England—Massachusetts, Connecticut, New Hampshire, Rhode Island and Vermont. To these Maine, hitherto a dependency of Massachusetts, was added as a separate state in 1820.

In the early days of the American republic the Commonwealth, as it is called, of Massachusetts dominated the northern states, just as Virginia did the southern. Massachusetts was the centre of an aristocratic tradition which, unwillingly though it might admit the fact, it derived from England. It was a tradition of landowners and country gentlemen. It was not, as in Virginia, a tolerant tradition. It was puritanical and narrow; it had a high moral sense and it possessed a conscience as sensitive as any known to history. Nowhere is the intimate connection between unbending puritanical faith and the rise of capitalism better illustrated than in New England in the eighteenth and nineteenth centuries. New England remains something of a byword for social exclusiveness and moral and religious intolerance, but it is probably no longer true that in Boston, "the home of the bean and the cod":

> Lowells speak only to Cabots
> And Cabots speak only to God.

The New England tradition was also a cultured and literary one In the earliest days of the Massachusetts colony, a seat of higher learning was established at Cambridge on the Charles River, and named from its founder, Harvard. Yale University, founded at New Haven, Connecticut, followed, together with a host of lesser colleges: Amherst, Brown, Dartmouth, Williams. New England was the home of a distinguished group of literary figures: Oliver Wendell Holmes, Emerson, Thoreau and Washington Irving were New Englanders. In the nineteenth century, New England was a focus of culture in this raw, vigorous, expansive and rather barbaric continent.

But the primacy of New England has ended. The centres of industry have moved across the Appalachians; the focus of trade is no longer Boston, but New York and the Gulf and Pacific ports. In the nineteenth century the Irish began to settle in Boston, to be joined later by Poles and other immigrants from Central Europe. The politics of Boston are now virtually controlled by the Irish group. The austere New Englanders are outnumbered by Roman Catholics, and there are now at Boston a Cardinal Archbishop and a Jesuit university. How affairs have changed since the days of John Winthrop, or even of Nathaniel Hawthorne!

At its western extremity, along the shores of Long Island Sound and up the Housatonic Valley, New England is becoming a dormitory for city workers who "commute" daily to New York City. South-western Connecticut is becoming an industrial suburb of New York. At the opposite ends of the state, the mountains of Vermont and New Hampshire, and the forests and island-fringed coast of Maine are growing into one of the foremost resort areas of the United States. Luxury hotels have replaced the log-cabins of the pioneers. From all parts of the Union people come for the skiing in winter, for the coolness of the mountain breezes in summer, and for the glory of the autumn colours.

THE PHYSICAL GEOGRAPHY OF NEW ENGLAND. New England consists essentially of two ranges of mountains extending from north to

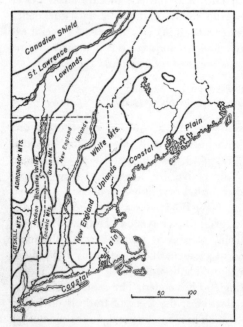

south and separated by the valley of the Connecticut River. In the north the two ranges come together, and broken, mountainous country extends north-eastwards along the Canadian border. The more westerly of these ranges is the Green Mountains with their southerly continuations, the Berkshire Mountains and the Taconic Mountains. The more easterly range culminates in the White Mountains of New Hampshire. Both ranges become lower towards the south and die away in the low, rounded hills of Connecticut. A narrow strip of lowland lies along the Hudson Valley, to the west

Fig. 15. NEW ENGLAND: RELIEF REGIONS

of the Green Mountains. A broader plain, generally from twenty to forty miles wide, borders the ocean all the way from the limits of New York in the south to the boundary of Canada. It is on this plain that most of the cities and almost all the industries of New England are concentrated. Off the southern coast lies Long Island, politically a part of New York State and economically tied to the metropolis. East of Long Island is a succession of low islands, of which Martha's Vineyard and Nantucket are the largest. They are flat, sandy, wind-swept and almost treeless, but in summer are cool and refreshing after the heat of Boston or New York City.

The coast of New England is deeply indented and irregular, the pro-duct of a post-glacial "drowning" by a rise in sea level. A substantial part of Rhode Island consists of the inlets and islands which make up Narraganset Bay. Fifty miles further to the east is the curving promon-tory of Cape Cod, composed, like the offshore islands, of glacial sands and gravels, re-sorted and deposited by the waves of the sea. It is a resort during the summer months chiefly because the high tempera-tures are here lowered by the cool breezes from the ocean.

At the head of Massachusetts Bay are the smaller, island-studded inlets around which the city of Boston and its spreading suburbs (fig. 18) are grouped. Further to the north, in Maine, the coast becomes even more rugged and beautiful, and the islands more numerous. The mountains of the interior give rise to many rivers—the Kennebec and Penobscot are the largest—which tumble down from the mountains to their deep, forest-fringed estuaries. Along the coast are numerous fishing ports, from which schooners sail to the Grand Banks (see p. 171). No physical change marks the international boundary between the United States and Canada. Drowned estuaries and islands continue into New Brunswick and Nova Scotia, which in their physical characteristics resemble New England (see Chapter 12).

The whole of New England was glaciated. The hills of the interior were scoured and denuded of soil; the lower ground received an un-even spread of boulder clay. Its fields are strewn with rocks, which the farmer removes and builds into the walls that enclose his fields, and the surface of the ground is broken by rounded drumlins and fragments of moraine.

American writers often comment on the variety of landscape in New England; it "is essentially a patchwork of small regions of varied charac-ter".[1] To an Englishman the regions of New England would not seem small. Most of New England is made up of a dissected plateau, or pene-plain. Basins and valleys have been cut into it, and above its surface rise the mountain ranges and the isolated mountains, of which one,

[1] J. K. Wright, in *New England's Prospect: 1933*, American Geographical Society (New York, 1933), p. 14.

Mount Monadnock, has given its name to this type of residual mountain.[1] The traveller passes through a continuously changing panorama of rounded hills, separated by valleys whose level floors are often under crops or pasture. As the valley turns one gets distant glimpses of the blue line of the White or Green Mountains. The scene resembles in some respects the Welsh Border or southern Scotland, but there is more woodland than one ever sees in England. The hill-sides are generally under forest: the soil is too thin and poor to be used in any other way.

The climate of New England is severe. Winters are long, very cold and very snowy. The summer is hot in the valleys and along the coastal plain, though cooler in the mountains of the interior. The growing season for plants is short. Only near the sea does it exceed 150 days, and over much of the interior it is less than 100 days. The poor, stony soil, the relative scarcity of level land and the extreme climate combine to make New England a harsh land. It is surprising indeed, that it is as populous and as industrialized as we find it to be. It is possible that

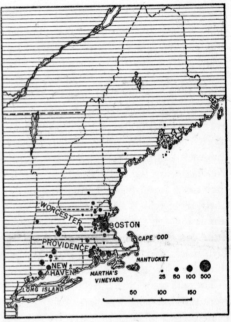

Fig. 16. NEW ENGLAND: CITIES

if any people less tough and less stubborn than the unbending Puritans of the seventeenth century had been brought to these shores, their stay might have been relatively short.

POPULATION AND SETTLEMENT. The history of population in the United States is one of continuous growth. In New England alone have

[1] This is the *locale* of W. M. Davis's classic analysis of the peneplanation cycle in "The Physical Geography of Southern New England", in *The Physiography of the United States* (New York, 1896), pp. 269–304.

there been greater vicissitudes. The original population was of English stock; we have seen how it has been replaced in the cities by more recent immigrants from central and southern Europe. In the rural areas population reached a maximum in the middle years of the nineteenth century and since then has been in decline. There has been a veritable flight from the stony fields of New Hampshire and Vermont, and in Massachusetts, despite the demand for farm produce created by nearby Boston and New York, abandoned fields and decaying farmsteads are an all too common sight.[1] This decline in agriculture springs

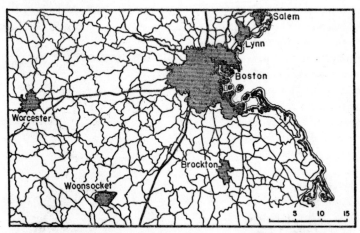

Fig. 17. THE PATTERN OF ROADS IN A PART OF NEW ENGLAND
Compare with figs. 22 and 24. The heavy lines indicate modern
turnpike highways.

from the fact that crops can be grown in other parts of the United States and marketed in New England more cheaply than they can be grown in its own unrewarding soils. There is, however, a movement into the hills of New England. This region, harsh by comparison with other parts of the United States, nevertheless offers opportunities to the hard-working, thrifty French Canadian accustomed to the even harsher environment of the province of Quebec. The number of French Canadians employed as farmers or lumbermen is increasing in the rural areas, as that of Irish, Poles and Italians is in the cities. In Boston, the Cardinal Archbishop is heir to the spiritual dominance of the Pilgrim Fathers, and in the valleys of the interior a French-speaking Catholic is tending to replace the Puritan farmer. The character of

[1] There is an interesting comment on the abandonment of rural settlement in New England in A. J. Toynbee, *A Study of History*, Vol. II, pp. 65-73.

New England is being altered with the change in the nature of its population. There are many who lament the passing of the old type of New Englander. He has, however, only joined in the westward movement; the descendants of the Massachusetts settlers are now scattered through every state in the Union.

Boston remains to-day, as it has been for three centuries, the largest and the most important urban settlement of New England. It occupies a small, undulating area of low-lying ground—the Boston Basin—at the head of Massachusetts Bay. The drumlins, which give rise to the unevenness of the land extend into the bay where they form peninsulas and islands. Bunker Hill, defended by the intrepid revolutionaries of 1776, was in fact only a drumlin[1]. The present city centre is the Boston of the seventeenth century with narrow streets and a congestion more English than American. The more recent developments have spread outwards from this nucleus. Four miles to the north-west of the centre of Boston is Cambridge, where, in 1636, John Harvard established the university which bears his name.

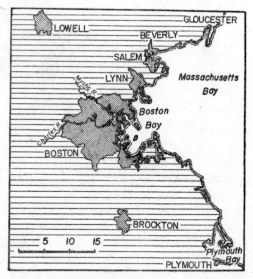

Fig. 18. THE SITE OF BOSTON

Boston is to-day an industrial city, with leather, textile and engineering industries. It is the foremost fishing port of the United States; it is the chief American market for wool and is a commercial port of considerable importance. The city of Boston in 1950 had a population of 801,444, making it the ninth largest city in the United States. The metropolitan area of Boston, which includes Quincy, Cambridge and other cities, has about 1,300,000. The population of Boston has risen slightly during the past generation though at a much slower rate than that of the nation as a whole.

[1] The monument which to-day commemorates this battle has, by an error of historical judgment, been placed on the wrong drumlin.

Along the Merrimac Valley to the north-west of Boston are the textile towns of Lowell, Lawrence and Haverhill. All have suffered from the depression in the New England cotton industry (see p. 71), and their population in recent years has shown a continuous decline. The cities themselves have that air of depression with which Englishmen are unhappily familiar. They display the architectural extravagances of the Victorian era of prosperity, overlain with the grime of almost a century. There is a notable absence of new buildings, and even the old are barely kept in repair. There is a fundamental similarity between these cities and Bury, Oldham or Merthyr Tydfil.

West of Boston are Worcester (203,486) and Springfield (162,399), and to the south Fall River (111,963), Providence (248,674), New Bedford (109,189) all of them suffering from the decline of the textile industry and, if not actually declining in population, barely holding their own.

The towns of the three northern states are all small (see fig. 16), but in Connecticut is a more lively growth, e.g. Stamford (74,293), Bridgeport (158,709) and Hartford (177,397).

AGRICULTURE. The original subsistence agriculture of the early settlers has given place to types of farming more specialized in their nature and more suited to the physical conditions. Dairying has tended to replace crop-farming, being encouraged both by the nearby markets for liquid milk and also by the suitability of the area for the growth of grass and fodder crops. There are, nevertheless, certain crops which are locally of great importance. To the south-west and along the Connecticut Valley tobacco is grown on a considerable scale. In north-eastern Maine and especially in Aroostock County, potatoes are a crop of great importance. Amongst the sandy barrens of south-eastern Massachusetts are the cranberry bogs, where is produced a significant proportion of the cranberries that Americans eat, as a pleasant patriotic duty, together with their turkey at Thanksgiving time. Sweet corn and vegetables are grown. Apple orchards and poultry farms are found along the New England valleys.

Specialization is proving to be the salvation of New England agriculture, but, even so, there are few crops for which the long and bitter winters and the shallow soils, of upper Vermont and New Hampshire and the hills of Maine, recommend themselves.

Forest industries have always been important in New England. Most of the region was originally thickly covered with hardwood trees, with softwoods over the mountains of the north. Much of the forest cover has been cut over, but it quickly reasserts itself. Abandoned farms have been found after a generation to have a sturdy growth of young trees. The lumber industry to-day is by no means as important as in the nineteenth century, when the logs were floated down to the coast of Maine, the furniture industry of Massachusetts was supplied with timber from nearby forests, and fresh settlements were being built of wood. Much of the forest has been depleted, but there is a pulpwood industry in the mountains, New England produces part of her annual lumber requirements and in Maine the sugar maple is still tapped in winter for its syrup, an interesting if now unimportant survival.

THE FISHERIES. The fishing industry of New England was encouraged by the great wealth in fish of the shallow seas that lie off the New England coast (see p. 171), by the facility with which schooners could be built and operated from its many bays and estuaries, and by the ungrateful soil which, from the earliest days of settlement, directed men's attention to the harvest of the sea.

To-day the chief fishing ports are Boston, which takes almost half the New England catch, and many smaller ports lying further to the north: among them Gloucester, Portsmouth and Portland. Over half the fish landed are cod and haddock, while lobsters and shellfish make up a considerable proportion of the remainder. Boston has the freezing and packing stations for handling large quantities of fish, but at the smaller ports, where the mechanism of packing and transportation is less developed, much of the fish is opened and dried, as in Newfoundland, on wooden racks built along the shore.

MANUFACTURING INDUSTRIES. Manufacturing industries had an early start in New England. The Massachusetts settlers, having little that they could sell to Europe, were obliged to make themselves a good deal of their requirements in cloth and metal goods. The hundreds of rivers descending from the mountains of New Hampshire and Vermont later offered a source of power, and the farm stock of the early settlers provided wool and hides, raw materials of some of the first industries to be established. The New England water supply was soft, and suited to the processing of textiles. A body of skilled labour was developed, and the skills were perpetuated and extended in the trade schools of the Massachusetts towns.

Until the middle years of the nineteenth century New England was the most strongly industrialized area of the continent. It is true that

NSPORT: (I) A MAIN ROAD IN PENNSYLVANIA. *The intensity of the fast road traffic necessitates leaf road junctions, to avoid the need for vehicles to cross in front of one another.* (II) THE "PENN-ANIA TURNPIKE" *as it cuts across the Ridge-and-Valley region of the Appalachian Mountains.*

(I) PITTSBURGH (*facing east*). *To the left is the Allegheny River; to the right, the Monongahe River. The "down-town" area between the two rivers is known as the "Golden Triangle'*
(II) NEW ORLEANS. *Ships tie up at quays along the Mississippi River. The palm trees in t foreground are evidence of the sub-tropical climate.*

the smelting of iron, which had never been of considerable importance, disappeared, but the production of cotton and woollen textiles, the tanning of leather and making of footwear, the pulp and paper industries and engineering developed and took a firm grip on the area. Local water power ceased to be sufficient. The high cost of importing coal was offset by the advantage offered by the reserve of skilled labour and the capital equipment of the region.

During the present century, however, New England has begun to lose some of the advantages she formerly possessed. With the westward spread of population, the larger part of the American market has ceased to lie at her door. The increasing mechanization of industrial processes has deprived the skilled New England labour of the high value which it formerly possessed. Lastly the lack of fuel and the almost complete absence of industrial raw materials from New England is increasing the costs of industrial production. New England is not declining as a centre of factory industry, but the kind of industry carried on is changing. The typical New England industry to-day is that which uses a comparatively small amount of raw material, which makes small demands on fuel and power and which adds a very great deal to the value of the materials by processing them. The manufacture of machine tools, of textile machinery and of other mechanical appliances can be regarded as typical New England industries.

On the other hand, manufactures, long regarded as traditional in this area, are in decline. At the beginning of the present century over two-thirds of the cotton spindles of the United States were in New England, most of them in the cotton towns of Rhode Island (Providence, Pawtucket, Woonsocket), Massachusetts (Fall River, Taunton, Lowell, Lawrence) and southern New Hampshire. Expensive labour and transport costs on the bulky raw material slowed down the development of the cotton industry in the present century. At the same time lower wage rates and a less vigorous trade union movement, were encouraging the industry in the southern states (see p. 123). By about 1920, the South had grown to an approximate equality with New England, and after that date gradually drew ahead. To-day, New England possesses only about one fifth of the nation's cotton spindles, while more than three-quarters are now found in the South.

The woollen and worsted industry of New England, while it never attained the size of the cotton, has shown a stronger disposition to remain. There is to-day a larger premium upon skill in these branches of the textile industry than in cotton. Most of the raw wool is imported; Boston has become the chief wool market of America, and the coastal

F

location of the industry in New England is as good as any. The chief
centres of manufacture are the same as for cotton: Lawrence, Lowell,
Providence, Woonsocket. The future of the woollen and worsted industry is nevertheless far from assured. Though the industry has not
declined appreciably in recent years, it is responsible for a diminishing
proportion of the total American output. There is at least a danger that
the site-value of New England may prove to be less than that of other
parts of the United States for the manufacture of woollen textiles as it
has done for cotton.

The production of leather goods also counts as a traditional New
England industry, based upon the early local supply of hides and the
local demand for footwear, harness and other articles of leather. The
local supply of hides is no longer sufficient for a large industry, and the
bulk of the American market for shoes is no longer within a short distance of Boston. About a third of the nation's shoes continues to be made
in the suburbs of Boston, but the rise of tanning and leather-consuming
industries to the west and south is likely to be accompanied by some
decline of the industry in New England.

In the paper industry and in others based on timber, the fortunes of
New England have been similar in recent years. Industrial growth has
failed to keep pace with that of the nation as a whole; factories have
been closed and replaced by others more favourably located with regard
to the supply of fuel and raw materials.

In some respects the industrial plight of New England resembles that
of England herself. A lead which both formerly enjoyed in the manufacturing industries has been lost; technological changes have deprived
both of some of the advantages they once possessed, and the future of
both probably lies in the manufacture of the highest quality goods,
whether textile or mechanical, which still call for the highest technical
skills.

If there is some measure of decline, depression and despondency in
the industrial centres that lie around Boston, this is not so with the more
south-westerly parts of New England. Here the expansion of New York
City, the growth of its port facilities and the development of a vast
market for consumer goods have encouraged the rise of a varied group of
manufacturing industries. These spread from the Bronx (see p. 58) and
the northern shore of Long Island Sound to Stamford, Bridgeport and
New Haven. Food processing industries, light and electrical engineering and chemical industries have sprung up. At the present time,
Bridgeport (Conn.) is the scene of a newly developed iron and steel industry, the iron ore for which will be brought by sea from South

America and the fuel from Pennsylvania. If the dependence of industry on foreign sources of raw materials increases further, it is possible that there may be a yet greater expansion of industries at this convenient focus of ocean shipping routes.

— 6 —

The Middle Atlantic Seaboard

SOUTHWARDS and westwards from New York City the coastal plain widens into a belt of country over a hundred miles in width. On the west it is bounded by the first of the ridges of the Appalachian Mountains; on the east by a low, flat, dune-fringed coast. The plain is far from level. Eastward-dipping beds of alternate soft and resistant rock give rise to low ridges. The more westerly part of the plain is in reality a low plateau, the Piedmont, dissected by rivers to a series of low hills and broad valleys. The more easterly is lower, and is developed in softer rocks which here overlie the harder rocks of the Piedmont. The boundary of these two regions is a break of slope, known as the Fall Line. In places it is a conspicuous feature of the landscape, as it is inland from Washington and Baltimore. Elsewhere it is worn back and is scarcely perceptible.

The region is crossed by four rivers of major importance: the Delaware, Schuylkill, Susquehanna and Potomac. Each rises deep within the Appalachian Mountains, follows a zig-zag course as it crosses the alternate ridges and valleys, and, escaping from the Blue Ridge by a narrow water gap, flows straight across the Piedmont towards the sea.

The coast here, as in New England, shows evidence of recent changes of sea level. The lower courses of all these rivers have been drowned and two enormous estuaries formed. The Schuylkill joins the Delaware to enter Delaware Bay. The Susquehanna and the Potomac, along with many smaller rivers from Virginia, flow into the immense land-locked waterway of Chesapeake Bay. This estuary is about 180 miles from north to south. Its width varies from 15 to over 30 miles across. The Potomac, Rappahannock and James Rivers themselves broaden into quite considerable estuaries which are tributary to the bay itself.

The shores of both Chesapeake and Delaware Bays are generally low and marshy and there are very few settlements. Along the Atlantic

coast, however, from
Sandy Hook, at the
entrance to New York
harbour, southwards
to Cape Charles at
the entrance to the
Chesapeake is a suc-
cession of offshore
bars and low islands,
built of the sand piled
up by the winds from
the ocean. Here is a
succession of resorts
which range from the
garish sophistication
of Atlantic City to
collections of small
beach shacks.

It is only about 230
miles from New York
to Washington, at the
extremities of this re-
gion. The fast trains,
which leave the Pen-
nsylvania Railroad
terminal in New York
at hourly intervals,

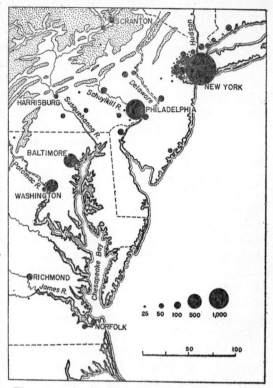

Fig. 19. THE ATLANTIC SEABOARD, FROM NEW
YORK TO VIRGINIA: CITIES AND TRANSPORT

cover the distance in four hours. The modern dual lane turnpike, now
more than half completed, will allow the motorist to cover the distance
between the political and the business capitals of the nation even faster
than the train is able to do. Yet in these few hours the traveller passes
from the gateway to New England to the borders of the "South". This
region is a transitional one between the New England climate, with
its long winters and short-growing season, and the hot, humid region,
where cotton and rice flourish. In March and April one can see the
spring creep slowly northwards along the middle Atlantic plain, and in
September the Fall marches southward from New England to Virginia,
burning up the trees in deep red flames and leaving till spring only their
blackened trunks. The growing season near New York is 160 days; at
Washington it is 200. This is sufficient comment on the climatic difference between the extremities of our region.

AGRICULTURE. Despite these contrasts, however, there is no great variety in the agricultural land use of the region. The soils are poor over most of the area. Much of the Piedmont has a heavy clay soil that does not till well. Over the coastal plain there are large areas both of damp and ill-drained soil and also of dry and infertile sands. Nevertheless, the proximity of the large cities of New York, Philadelphia and Washington necessitates the use of land which in other parts of the United States might go uncultivated.

The sandy tract near the sea is the scene of the intensive cultivation of vegetables for the city markets. The sandy soil warms up quickly in the spring, and the proximity of the ocean has the effect of increasing the frost-free period, but a very heavy use of fertilizer is necessary in a soil as easily leached as this. Elsewhere a mixed farming is practised with a certain emphasis on the production of milk.

In south-eastern Pennsylvania, on each side of the Susquehanna Valley is a small area outstanding for the high level of its farming. This is the so-called "Pennsylvania Dutch" area. It is, in contrast with the clays which cover much of the Piedmont, floored with limestone, and the quality of both arable and pasture is higher than in other parts of the region. But, as soil is "a response to management", so the excellence of this rolling country around Lancaster and York is due primarily to the effort and the care of the German farmers who came in early in the eighteenth century.[1] The "Dutch" countryside is wonderfully cared for. Nowhere is there any evidence of the untidy wilderness that makes up so much of the American countryside. Farm buildings are simple and good; the barns, vast and opulent. Nowhere in North America has farmland such an appearance of fatness and wealth; nowhere also is an acre worth more.

CITIES AND INDUSTRIES. The wealth of the Middle Atlantic seaboard lies in its cities rather than in its farms. In the Piedmont is a line of towns: Bethlehem (66,340), Allentown (106,756), Reading (109,320), Lancaster (63,774), Harrisburg (89,544), York (59,953). Bethlehem and Allentown are amongst the oldest centres of the American iron-smelting and steel-making industry and they still use to some extent the iron ore mined from the neighbouring ridge-and-valley region. Reading is no longer a metallurgical centre in the first instance, but has become a centre of the textile industry. These cities derive some industrial ad-

[1] The "Pennsylvania Dutch" are of course "Deutsch" who were forced to leave Germany in the late seventeenth and early eighteenth centuries, chiefly on account of their religious tenets. Most of them belong to the austere sect of the Amish.

vantage from the anthracite field, which lies to the north-west, within the limits of the ridge-and-valley region (see p. 83).

The region, however, is dominated by four urban agglomerations. New York City with the adjoining cities of Newark (438,776), Jersey City (299,017), Elizabeth (112,817) and others, each of them a large city in its own right, lie at the north-eastern extremity of the region. Together they make up an untidy, unplanned development. The towns run into one another, or are separated only by patches of second-growth woodland and vegetable plots on the marshy banks of the rivers that flow down to New York harbour.

Philadelphia. Not more than forty miles of open country separate the last of cities of the New York area from the first of those that en-circle Philadelphia. Philadelphia (2,071,605) is the third largest city in the United States, and is girdled by a ring of smaller cities: Trenton (128,009), Camden (124,555), Wilmington (110,356) and others. Philadelphia was established by William Penn, the Quaker founder of the Commonwealth of Pennsylvania on the north-western bank of the Delaware River, close to the junction of the Schuylkill, and ninety miles from the ocean. From the first the site of Philadelphia was favourable for ocean commerce; its immediate hinterland was in early days more populous and more productive than that of New York. The routes westwards to the anthracite field and across the Appalachian Moun-tains to the Ohio Valley were opened up in the later eighteenth century. For a long period Philadelphia enjoyed, with Boston, a position of primacy amongst the ports of the United States. This supremacy it gradually lost during the early nineteenth century as New York de-veloped its "sea-level" route along the Hudson and Mohawk Valleys to the Great Lakes and the Mid-West.

In the early years of its growth Philadelphia was dominated by the Quakers. For many years now the Quaker has been as inconspicuous in Philadelphia as the "Yankee" in Boston, and, as in Boston, the pro-portion of foreign-born population and of population of Central and South European ancestry is large.

The older parts of Philadelphia have a character not unlike that of the centre of Boston, though the city is laid out on a rectilinear pattern. Independence Hall and other buildings survive from the pre-revolu-tionary period, and Philadelphia was for a time, before the establish-ment of Washington, the seat of the American Government. Along the waterfront has developed a very extensive commercial port, and manu-facturing industries have been established along both banks of the

Delaware. Philadelphia is the largest producer of railway locomotives in the United States. It has engineering, oil refining and chemical industries, and to these has now been added the vast new Fairless iron and steel works of the American Steel Corporation. The city's industries tend to be those that depend to a large extent on imported raw materials. America is now importing considerable quantities of iron ore, and the newest iron and steel works are on the coast. To the west of the city, on the higher ground above the "fall line", is a large and growing residential area, which retains some evidence of the Quaker respectability that has vanished from "down-town" Philadelphia. Here, too, is a sizeable group of colleges which minister to the needs for "higher" education.

Baltimore (949,708) lies nearly a hundred miles to the south-west of Philadelphia. In its location and history it resembles its larger neighbour. It was established early in the eighteenth century as a port, and it came to be the Atlantic terminus of the route which followed the Potomac River across the Appalachian Mountains. The earliest modern railway in the United States was the Baltimore and Ohio, whose first objective it was to reach the Ohio Valley from Baltimore. But Baltimore has failed to keep pace with the growth of Philadelphia and New York. It has no ring of satellites, and its port facilities and manufacturing industries are less developed than those of its neighbours.

The industries of Baltimore are closely associated with its sea-borne commerce: oil and sugar refining, the preparation of foodstuffs, the manufacture of fertilizers and the smelting of non-ferrous metals. The Bethlehem Steel Corporation has established a large iron-smelting and steel-making plant at Sparrows Point on the shore of Chesapeake Bay near the city.

Baltimore retains more of the character of an eighteenth century town than any other in the United States, with the possible exception of Boston. Its houses built in terrace pattern, with a few steps or "stoops", always painted white and kept meticulously clean, rising to the front doors, its bow-fronted shop windows along Charles Street and the air of massive dignity that characterizes its buildings, all combine to lift Baltimore above the dull uniformity that characterizes most American cities.

Washington (802,178) is quite different from all other American cities. The site was chosen and the streets laid out in a manner worthy of the capital of the American nation. The choice of a capital had caused much feeling between the original thirteen states. A compromise was to acquire a tract of land by purchase from one or more of the states and to establish it as a federal capital, removed from the influence and the pressures that a state might be able to bring to bear. Thus was acquired the District of Columbia, an area ten miles square, spanning the Potomac and taken part from Maryland, part from Virginia. The city of Washington was first planned about 1800 on the northern or Maryland bank. The tract beyond the Potomac was later found to be redundant and was handed back to Virginia.

Almost all American cities have been planned but for none was the plan as elaborate as that drawn up by Charles L'Enfant for Washington. In addition to wide streets intersecting at right-angles, the architect proposed a series of diagonals which would converge on the salient buildings in the city. The plan was never completed in its entirety, but the portion built is one of the finest example of urban planning in North America. At the centre of L'Enfant's plan is an avenue with wide lawns and trees, running east from the Potomac River. To the north was built the White House, or presidential mansion; at its eastern end the Capitol in which Congress meets. At the western end, close to the river, has been built in more recent years the very dignified memorial to President Lincoln, and at its middle point, south of the White House, an immense granite obelisk commemorates the President from whom the city is named. Government offices line this central parkway and stretch out along the avenues that radiate from the Capitol and White House. The shopping area lies to the north and beyond it a vast residential area rises up over the "fall line" and across the rolling country beyond.

The business of governing is the only industry in Washington. There are no factories and little smoke. It is a clean city. Its wide streets and avenues and many parks give it an air of spaciousness which few other cities in the world possess. Most of its buildings have a dignity befitting (though rarely found in) a great capital. Lying, as it does, on the borders of Virginia, it has a winter that is rarely cold, and snow seldom lies long on the ground. On the other hand, the southerly latitude, combined with the low-lying site beside the marshy Potomac, makes the summers hot and oppressive in the extreme. For days in succession in July and August both temperature and relative humidity are in the high nineties, and all who can, escape from the city either to the mountains or to the shores of the Chesapeake.

Washington is on the boundary of North and South. A wide bridge, behind the Lincoln Memorial, spans the Potomac. Beyond it are the low hills of Virginia and here, facing northwards across the river to the city of Washington is the mansion of Robert E. Lee, commander of the Confederate or Southern forces in the Civil War. Here, across the Potomac River, the coloured people become relatively numerous. They cease to sit with the white in the street-car, to eat at the same table, or even to use the same restaurant. There may be no cotton in the fields, but this is the beginning of the South.

– 7 –

The Appalachian Mountains

THE Appalachian Mountains rise abruptly along the western margin of the Piedmont (see pp. 74 and 113). From out on the plain they appear to constitute an unbroken wall of uniform height stretching all the way from Pennyslvania and New Jersey to Georgia and Alabama. It is not surprising that they deterred the early settlers from pressing into the interior of the continent. In reality this most easterly range of the Appalachian system is broken by several gaps, some of them followed by rivers, but the traveller who penetrates these openings is faced by more mountain ridges, forested to their summits, lying one behind the other as if drawn up to repel travellers from penetrating the interior of the continent. To-day the roads pass from one gap to another, and by a zig-zag course make their way across this region of ridge and vale without climbing over the summits of any but the lower ridges. But at last an unbroken mountain wall faces the traveller, without gap and valley to assist his passage. This is the Allegheny Front. It is not a ridge like the mountains encountered hitherto, but rather the steep eastern face of a plateau, whose undulating surface, scarred by the deep valleys of rivers flowing to the Ohio, drops very gently westwards until it passes into the plains of the Mid-West and of the Mississippi basin.

THE APPALACHIAN SYSTEM. These, then, are the threefold divisions of the Appalachian system: first, a high eastern ridge which preserves a remarkable continuity for 400 miles, and which for much of its length is known as the Blue Ridge, though towards the south it broadens into the rugged mass of the Great Smoky Mountains. Secondly, west of it is the Ridge and Valley region, in which a maze of short segments of mountain are aligned roughly parallel with the Blue Ridge. Thirdly, there is the Allegheny Plateau. Fig. 21 shows a cross-section through the Appalachian Mountains in Pennsylvania. The three

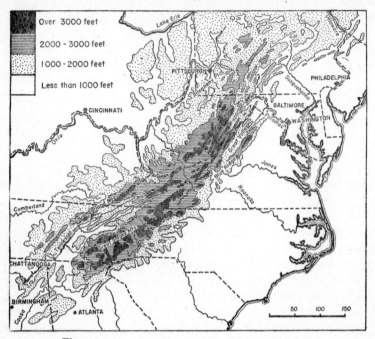

Fig. 20. APPALACHIAN MOUNTAINS: RELIEF MAP

provinces mentioned are seen to extend through the whole length of the Appalachian Mountains.

The geological history of the Appalachian system is highly complex. A mountain range was formed at the end of the Palaeozoic by the folding of thick deposits of primary beds. The folding was accompanied by some faulting and overthrusting, but the complex overfolding of alpine type was absent. This mountain region was then eroded and reduced to a peneplain above which only a few areas rose to any considerable height. The folded beds outcropped in narrow belts lying roughly from north-north-east to south-south-west, on the surface of the peneplain. The peneplain was then uplifted probably unevenly, and eroded by rivers. These incised their courses into the surface of the peneplain, eroding the softer beds and forming narrow water-gaps through the ridges of more resistant rock. Over a long period of time the rivers adjusted their courses to the geological structure. By process of capture the drainage pattern was gradually modified and the present trellis-pattern was evolved.

The threefold division of the Appalachian Mountains into the Blue

Ridge and its southward extension, the Great Smoky Mountains; the Ridge-and-Valley province; and the high and dissected plateaux lying further to the west, accords closely with structural and stratigraphic differences.

The Blue Ridge and Great Smoky Mountains. The Blue Ridge in the narrow sense begins at the Schuylkill River in eastern Pennsylvania and extends for 600 miles into northern Georgia. Between the Schuylkill and the Susquehanna Rivers, it is worn down to a few low ridges, and south of the Susquehanna it reaches no great heights. The barrier to westward movement is formed here not by the Blue Ridge but rather by the mountains of the Ridge-and-Valley province. But south of the Potomac the Blue Ridge assumes the proportions of a mountain range. As far as Roanoke in Virginia, it is a narrow belt of rugged country, at most fifteen miles across, which rises steeply from the Piedmont on the east and the Great Valley on the west to heights of over 4,000 feet. The crest of the Blue Ridge is far indeed from level. Rounded, dome-like mountains succeed one another, and the road that follows the ridge rises and falls, with a constantly changing panorama to the west across the Ridge-and-Valley, and to the east across the rolling plain of the Piedmont.

The Blue Ridge is made up of crystalline or metamorphic rocks, resistant to erosion. South of Roanoke these rocks become more massive; the ridge widens into the mountain mass whose highest parts are known as the Great Smoky Mountains. The mountains die away a short distance within the borders of Georgia, and the Piedmont wraps round their southern extremity (see p. 113).

The whole region is forested; the steep slopes and the poor soil have never attracted settlers. But to-day it is opened up by good motor roads and its accessibility to the large cities of north-eastern United States has made it a summer resort. The Blue Ridge in Virginia and the Great Smoky Mountains both constitute National Parks and are amongst the greatest scenic attractions of the continent.

North-east of the Schuylkill River the direction of the Blue Ridge is continued towards the Hudson River by a series of hills of little more than a thousand feet in altitude. These overlook the Hudson in the high cliffs above West Point, and are continued structurally beyond the river in the mountains of New England.

The Ridge-and-Valley Province. To the west of the Blue Ridge is a strip of lower land, the Great Valley. In parts, as in the Shenandoah Valley, it is a wide, rich lowland. Elsewhere, as in the valleys of the New and Holston Rivers, it is merely a rift, pinched out between the Blue Ridge and the countless ridges of the next reigon to the west. It is imposs- ible to enumerate the ridges which compose this province. Fig. 21, which illustrates only a small area of eastern Pennsylvania, demonstrates their number. In general they are forested. The narrow strips of lower land which separate them are under cultivation, but agriculture is restricted in many parts by the cooler conditions, which result from the greater altitude, and by the long and snowy winter.

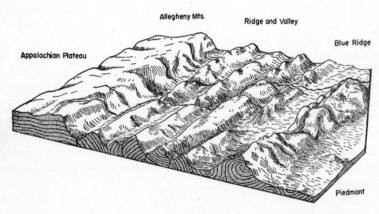

Allegheny Mts.

Ridge and Valley

Blue Ridge

Appalachian Plateau

Piedmont

Fig. 21. APPALACHIAN MOUNTAINS: DIAGRAMMATIC SKETCH OF RELIEF REGIONS

Wherever it is crossed, the Ridge-and Valley province has a peculiar fascination. The successive ridges, which must have tried severely the patience of the early settlers, offer a succession of studies in erosion and in land use. The dry gaps and truncated streams show the processes of river capture. In their sometimes bare slopes and the precipices that overhang the streams can be seen the naked structure of this region.

In south-western Virginia the ridges cluster more closely; the general level of the land rises, and a watershed is passed separating the rivers that follow a generally northward direction from those which flow south-westwards to make the Tennessee. Here in the valleys of the Clinch, Holston and French Broad we enter the valley of the Tennessee, scene not only of some of the greatest destruction of natural resources in the United States, but also of the greatest American experiment in planned land-use.

The agricultural resources of the Ridge-and-Valley province are slender. Much of the farm land is under grass; the steeper slopes under forest. Towns are few and small. The city map of North America shows none of even modest size except in a small area to the north-east where anthracite is mined, giving rise to an industrial area Electric power is a major resource of the more southerly part of the region. It is generated at power stations built along the Tennessee and its tributaries, and is leading to some industrial growth in the southern Appalachians.

The Allegheny Mountains and Plateau. The finest views across the Ridge-and-Valley country are to be had from the rim of the Allegheny Plateau. This escarpment extends with no appreciable break all the way from the Hudson River, above New York, to central Alabama. It rises to heights greatly exceeding 4,000 feet, and the steepness of its slope adds to its mountainous appearance. Behind it is the Allegheny Plateau, built of nearly horizontal rocks, amongst which hard sand-stones predominate. The plateau surface is not level; a slight flexing of the beds may bring a harder rock to the surface, producing a ridge which rises a few hundred feet above the plateau surface. The plateau is etched by the ravine-like valleys of the many westward flowing rivers. The railways follow these valleys wherever possible, but roads are more often compelled to cross one deep wooded valley after another, necessi-tating repeated steep descents and ascents. In southern Pennsylvania the problem is in some measure solved by the "Pennsylvania Turnpike", a well engineered highway which follows for much of its course from Philadelphia to Pittsburgh (327 miles) the bed of an unfinished rail-way. It crosses the ridges and also the Allegheny Mountains by means of a series of tunnels.

Towards the west the level of the plateau drops. In the north it passes almost imperceptibly into the plains of Ohio, but in general its western margin is marked by a scarp, less precipitous and imposing than that which looks eastward across the Ridge-and-Valley, but never-theless visible from far out across the plains of the Mid-West.

Though continuous almost from the valley of the Mohawk River and the shore of Lake Erie into Alabama, this plateau is divisible on physical grounds into a number of smaller units. In the extreme north, the plateau was glaciated during the Pleistocene Period. The ice led to ex-tensive changes in the drainage pattern. Moraines closed the outlets of many valleys, leading to the formation of the "finger lakes" which are one of the delights of upper New York State. One area of the northern plateau escaped the glaciation. The Catskill Mountains were almost enveloped by the ice-sheet, but their summits rose above its surface. These are a mass of sandstone which has resisted the forces of erosion more strongly than other rocks of the region, and to-day forms a dissected and rugged region rising above the peneplained surface of the plateau. The Catskill Mountains are to-day a thickly forested region, which serves as a water-catchment area for New York City and as a resort for its inhabitants.

South of the glacial limit the region has the appearance of a deeply dissected plateau. Two of the Atlantic rivers, the Susquehanna and the Potomac, rise within the limits of the plateau and flow eastwards across the Ridge-and-Valley towards the Piedmont and the sea, but most of the plateau is drained westwards towards the Ohio. A number of the

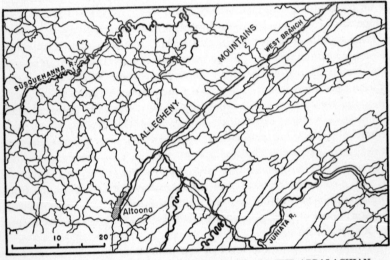

Fig. 22. THE PATTERN OF ROADS IN A PART OF THE APPALACHIAN MOUNTAINS

Note the contrast between the pattern in the Ridge-and-Valley region to the east and in the Allegheny Plateau to the west.

streams in the more northerly part of the plateau join the Allegheny and Monongahela Rivers, and these two come together at the "Forks of the Ohio", famous in colonial history, where they unite to form the Ohio. The wide Ohio takes a deep and winding valley across the plateau, escaping from the last of its rounded outliers on the borders of Ohio and Kentucky. South of the Monongahela, other rivers, the Kanawha, Greenbrier and New, the Big Sandy, Kentucky, Cumberland and Duck, all trench the plateau from their sources near the eastern scarp to the points where the plateau at last expires on the margin of the central lowland.

In eastern Kentucky the plateau narrows to a belt of land rarely more than fifty miles wide. This is the Cumberland Plateau. Its surface is formed by rocks harder in general than those which compose the Allegheny Plateau, and the valleys of the rivers which cross it are even less maturely developed than those further to the north. Along its eastern margin the Cumberland Plateau rises a few hundred feet to the Cumberland Mountain, the southward continuation of the Allegheny Front. Here a scarp, as striking as any further to the north, overlooks the Ridge-and-Valley of eastern Tennessee.

THE SETTLEMENT AND DEVELOPMENT OF THE APPALACHIAN REGION. During the eighteenth century the Appalachian ridges and valleys were penetrated and settled by immigrants from the eastern coastal regions. Many routes were opened up. In the earlier days of the westward movement the "Wilderness Road" was the most used. This route traversed the Ridge-and-Valley province of Virginia, crossed the Cumberland Mountain by the Cumberland Gap and then threaded the deep valleys of the Cumberland Plateau. Other routes were opened up later. The Hudson-Mohawk route, at first blocked by the powerful confederation of the Iroquois Indians, subsequently grew to be the most important. Other routes followed the Susquehanna and Potomac Rivers and their tributaries, and, after portages across the Allegheny Front, picked up the headwaters of the west-flowing rivers. The convergence of these at the "Forks of the Ohio" made this a focus of early routeways across the Appalachians. It was a centre of commerce and of communications long before it became a centre of the iron and steel industries. We know it to-day as Pittsburgh.

Many passed through the gaps and valleys of the Appalachians to the Mid-West. Some remained along the routes, on the farms and in the small towns that sprang up. In most of the northern Appalachians, where the flow of people and of commerce has continued in growing volume, there was little sense of isolation. The mountain people remained in touch with the plainsmen. But the flow of immigrants across the southern Appalachians declined. The hills of Kentucky and Tennessee ceased to attract when the richer plains of Indiana and Illinois lay open and awaiting settlers. The settlers in the southern Appalachians were thus gradually cut off from the invigorating influence of new immigrants. The southern Appalachian mountaineer has tended to remain static, with the customs and language of the original settlers of two centuries ago, and content with living standards far below those of the nation as a whole. Tudor folk-songs and folk-dances (here called

G

square dances) are performed in a manner closely akin to that of six-teenth-century England. Words, long since lost from the English langu-age in other parts of the United States, still remain in current use. Ancient and often primitive beliefs and superstitions are retained.[1] The birth-rate amongst these highlanders is one of the highest in North America, and rural population is very dense in relation to the limited agricultural resources of the region. Transport is difficult in many parts, especially in the rugged Cumberland Plateau. Good roads are few, and railways even more rare. The hill people are driven to adopt a mode of living which is very nearly self-sufficing. Ignorance, poverty and an acute overpopulation have led to a serious misuse of the land. Slopes are steep and soil is shallow. Too much such land has been cultivated when it should have been left under forest cover. The soil has been eroded, the rivers choked and the agriculture of this region reduced to an even lower level of productivity.

The northerner views the southern Appalachian mountaineer with a mixture of pity and contempt. He sees his small, unpainted wooden shack, twisting out of shape as its supports rot for want of repair; the few patches of corn (maize) and the hogs which constitute his chief source of food; his scraggy horse or mule and the rough track that serves as a road. He attributes such conditions, according to his point of view, to innate laziness or original sin. He is not sensitive about the con-tinued existence of such poverty in the richest nation in the world.

The remedy lies in emigration from the southern Appalachians, in the introduction of better agricultural practices and in the industrializa-tion of the area. All these measures are in some degree being imple-mented. The more energetic are leaving the mountains to settle in the growing mill towns of the southern Piedmont. With the encouragement of the Tennessee Valley Authority, better modes of land use are being employed, gullying is being checked, steep slopes are being reafforested and contour ploughing introduced on sloping land. Lastly, factory in-dustries, encouraged by the production of electric power at the many stations along the Tennessee and its tributaries, are being brought into the southern Appalachian region. The atomic energy plant at Oak Ridge (Tenn.) is one example of this. Coal mining in Kentucky, Ten-nessee and Alabama is becoming increasingly important. Nevertheless, the hard core of the problem remains. There is a body of people who will not or cannot abandon their ancient, primitive mode of life.

---

[1] The play, *Dark of the Moon* by Howard Richardson and William Berney, which has been produced in London, recaptures in a remarkable fashion the ingenuous attitude of the southern mountaineer.

MINERAL RESOURCES. The rocks composing the Appalachians are mostly older than the coal measures, but coal is preserved in the level beds of the western plateaux and in parts of the intensely folded Ridge-and-Valley of eastern Pennsylvania. The latter is the anthracite field. It is made up of a number of narrow strips of coal-bearing ground, conforming in their general direction with that of the ridges amidst which they lie. The intense folding, to which the coal measures were subjected during the earth movements that built the Appalachian Mountains, hardened them, expelled their volatile constituents and converted them to anthracite. The most northerly field lies along the Susquehanna Valley, where it is flanked by mountains rising to over 2,000 feet. Mining towns succeed one another along the bottom of the valley in a manner reminiscent of a Welsh mining valley. There is a similar untidy development of spoil heaps, railway yards, and unsightly miners' cottages. The largest towns, Wilkes-Barre and Scranton, are the business centres of the field, with textile industries to employ those who are not taken by the mines.

Some ten miles to the south are the interconnected Eastern, Middle, Western Middle and Southern fields. These have larger reserves of coal than the northern, but the folding is more intense and the difficulties of mining are greater. Most of the settlements belong to the class of "mining village".

The demand for anthracite has diminished in recent years. It is not a fuel with many and varied uses. Its cleanliness and high heating value recommend it for domestic and office heating, but more and more natural gas and (crude) oil are replacing it. The output of the whole anthracite field, which had been almost 100,000,000 tons a year during the period of the First World War is now (1950) reduced to 44,077,000 tons.

The coal-field of the Allegheny Plateau, never subjected to the pressure of violent earth movement, yields a bituminous coal. The Appalachian coal-field extends, with only minute interruptions, from within a few miles of Lake Erie in the north to Birmingham (Ala) in the south, a distance of about 800 miles. The field is widest in the north—over 100 miles, narrowing in Kentucky and Tennessee, and expanding again in northern Alabama. Only a few scattered traces of coal occur in the Ridge-and-Valley province. The field commences in the Allegheny front and extends westwards to the limit of the plateau. Only in southeastern Tennessee and northern Alabama where rivers have cut into the plateau and removed the coal is there any break in its continuity. Along the eastern border of the field is a hard "steam" coal, but over most of the field is bituminous coal, which includes the coking coal for which parts of this area are famed. In the northern and southern extremes are gas coals.

The coal seams are throughout most of the field exceptionally level, and they attain thicknesses rarely found amongst the more contorted measures of Europe. The deep valleys which gouge the plateau make access to the seams easy. They are entered from the valley side. Often there is no shaft, except for ventilation, and coal, brought by truck to the mouth of the horizontal tunnels leading to the workings, is tipped into chutes which direct it into freight cars or river barges waiting in the valley below. This is a strangely picturesque mining area. Pit head-gear is rare, and many mines are lost in the greenery which enshrouds the valley sides.

The most intense production is in three areas, south-western Pennsylvania; southern West Virginia with neighbouring parts of Virginia and Kentucky, and northern Alabama. In the first area coal is mined along all the valleys converging on Pittsburgh: the Allegheny, Connemaugh, Youghioghenny and Monongahela. Connellsville, famous for its high grade coking coal, lies on the Youghiogheny. Each of these rivers, with turbid, grey, oil-stained waters, with tug-boats and coal barges, witnesses to the industrial activity that lies hidden amongst these wooded hills.

The second important centre of coal-mining lies about a hundred miles to the south-west, in the valleys of the Kanawha and its tributaries and along the border of the Cumberland Mountain. Rivers here are smaller and less easily navigated than those which join to make the Ohio. Fewer industries in this region use the coal, and a large part of it is sent east by rail to the coal port of Newport News on the Chesapeake. The third area of production lies far to the south, at the extremity of the coal-field in Alabama. Here mining attains a considerable importance around Birmingham, where the coal helps to support the local iron-smelting and steel industry. Between these areas of concentrated production are many where mining is carried on less intensively and yet more where it is a relatively unimportant supplement to agriculture.

Mining first attained importance in western Pennsylvania and neighbouring parts of Ohio and West Virginia, where communication both by river and by the early railroads was easiest. But the resources of the more southerly parts of the field are great and conditions of mining are in general superior to those in Pennsylvania and Ohio. There is a tendency for the focus of mining activity to move southwards. Development has been most marked in recent years in the southern part of West Virginia, in Virginia, Kentucky, Tennessee and Alabama. This is another illustration of a tendency, which we have already encountered in New England, for northern industries to decline or to increase less rapidly than southern (see p. 123).

One other mineral fuel is of small importance. The level beds underlying the Allegheny Plateau were formerly rich in petroleum. The first oil well in the continent was sunk in 1859 near Titusville, about eighty miles north of Pittsburgh. For most of the century Pennsylvania remained the chief producing area of the United States. Output declined rapidly during the present century, but in western Pennsylvania and eastern Ohio many hundreds of pumps are still at work. But the area has not the appearance of the conventional oil-field. The pumps, small, inconspicuous and operating automatically are tucked away in the corners of fields or hidden in woodlots, where they work silently, unobserved by the traveller. Occasionally a rotting wooden derrick rises beside the road to announce the fact that this is oil country.

In any other country iron-ore reserves such as those of the Appalachians would be reckoned important, but here they are dwarfed by the deposits of the Great Lakes region (see p. 108). Ores in the Ridge-and-Valley of eastern Pennsylvania supplied the earliest iron works in this region and are still worked to supply the furnaces at Bethlehem and Sparrows Point. Further north are considerable deposits in the Adirondack Mountains, and at Birmingham (Ala.) are the large resources that supply the iron works of the city.

MANUFACTURING INDUSTRIES. Only in the northern Appalachians have manufacturing industries assumed a great importance. The many towns that lie around the northern margin of the Allegheny Plateau have varied manufactures, most of them related to the huge market offered by New York and the great cities of the Atlantic coast. Clothing, textile and chemical industries have been moved out into the Appalachian towns from New York City in search of more space or to escape from restrictive labour conditions and regulations. But the dominant industries are coal, iron and steel production.

The early iron works of the eighteenth century lay along the valleys of the eastern Piedmont. They smelted the small, local ore deposits with charcoal and then with anthracite from the eastern Pennsylvania field. The iron and steel works at Bethlehem derive their origin from works of this kind. In the mid-nineteenth century anthracite from eastern Pennsylvania began to be replaced by coal from western. The coking qualities of the Connellsville coal were discovered, and began to attract the smelting industries westward. In the later years of the nineteenth century, furnaces and steel works sprang up at sites easily supplied with fuel. They lay along the Monongahela and Youghiogheny Rivers. Johnstown, on the Connemaugh, became a steel centre, and the industry reached out along the Ohio and Beaver Rivers to Youngstown, and down the Ohio to Weirton, Steubenville, Wheeling and Ashland. But the hub of all this industrial activity remained where the rivers from the Allegheny Plateau came together at the "Forks of the Ohio". Here the city of Pittsburgh grew up.

The strategic value of this site led to its fortification, first by the French as Fort Duquesne, and then as Fort Pitt. A log-built fort, dating from the early colonial days, is still preserved in the middle of the "Golden Triangle" between the Allegheny and Youghiogheny Rivers. The modern city has spread along the rivers and up over the plateau between them. Pittsburgh is now a city of 673,763 people, and, with the surrounding towns, makes up an urban development of over a million. The iron and steel industries lie along the river; the business and commercial centre lies in the angle between the two rivers, and the residential area spreads out over the higher ground. Pittsburgh is a busy, dirty city. Smoke from the industrial works lies along the valley, imparting a gloom as pervasive as that of industrial Lancashire and the Black Country.

The lesser industrial centres are better in this respect only because they emit less smoke. But they are not picturesque. They lie invariably along the valley bottom, close to the navigable waterway. The plateau slopes rise 500 to 1,000 feet above them, the trees slashed and the surface gullied. Rows of mean houses built of clapboard stand insecurely on the steep slopes. Roads are narrow; on shops and public buildings soot encrusts the over-abundant scrollwork and ornament. The much maligned Welsh mining valleys are no more ugly than such industrial towns as Monongahela, Johnstown and Steubenville.

The Pittsburgh region has a steel capacity of about 30,000,000 tons a year, about a third of the total of the United States. Coal and limestone are from the Allegheny Plateau, but the local reserves of iron ore, never large, have now been exhausted. The region depends on ore brought from the Lake Superior region, travelling by iron-ore boat as far as the Lake Erie ports and thence by rail to Pittsburgh.

A lesser steel centre has grown up at Lackawanna, a suburb of Buffalo. The works lie on the lake shore and are supplied with ore directly from the Great Lakes ore boats and with fuel from the Allegheny coal-field. South of the Pittsburgh region is a lesser centre of the smelting and steelmaking industries on the Kanawha Valley at Charleston (W. Va.) and on the Ohio River at Ashland (Ky.), but the most important centre outside the Pittsburgh region is at Birmingham (Ala.). A massive deposit of ore lies close to the city on the south-east and to the north-west are the almost level seams of the Warrior coal basin. Between lie abundant deposits of limestone and dolomite. Birmingham is, in consequence, a low cost producer of iron and steel. It lies comparatively far from the chief consuming centres in the north-east of the United States, but the growing demand in the South for iron and steel goods is providing a market for the Birmingham industries within short distances of the city.

The iron and steel centres of the Appalachians have ceased to be single-industry towns. Subsidiary industries have grown up close to the sites of the basic manufacture. Although mechanical engineering is not of great importance, such branches of industry as galvanizing and plating, the manufacture of wire and of wire goods, forgings and castings are important. Coke was formerly made in small beehive ovens in which the by-products were allowed to burn away. Such ovens are still to be seen, filling the valleys in which they operate with smoke and fumes, but in general they have been replaced by closed retorts, which allow the gases to be collected and processed. The numerous by-products obtained from the gases are the starting point of a series of chemical industries, and the gas that remains is used for heating in the steel works, or is burned in the domestic and office heating plant of Pittsburgh and other cities.

— 8 —

The Mid-West

No two people will define the Mid-West in the same way. The difficulty is that it is not a region to be defined in essentially physical terms, nor is it altogether an economic region. The Mid-West implies an attitude of mind. It is prosperous and wealthy. Long seclusion behind the barrier of the Appalachians, when the settlers were obliged to rely on their ingenuity, strength and courage, has led to a feeling of independence and self-reliance. There is a stronger sense of human equality here than in the East. Life is less sophisticated, education less sought after and the arts less cultivated. In political terms the Mid-West is generally rather conservative. Its view of the rest of the world is frequently a little naïve, and it periodically gives vent to expressions of that state of mind known as "isolationism". The Mid-West is a busy, thriving region; industry is a virtue—how unlike the South—and wealth is respected as the just reward of success. It is a region in which cultural values are not yet respected as they should be. There is something coarse in the blatant commercialism, in the pulsating, unfeeling activity, in the profit motif which runs through every human activity. But there is an incurable optimism and a complete lack of introspection; why should the successful be introspective? This is certainly not a decaying society. To some extent these characteristics belong to all America, but in the East and South their extravagances are moderated by the older civilization of these regions. The East and South have "values", but a sense of values develops only slowly in a newly settled land.

The Mid-West begins at the margin of the Allegheny Plateau. It stretches westwards across the plains; it ends, where the prosperity of the Mid-West farmer has its limit, in the dry grasslands and the "blown" areas of the Dakotas, Nebraska and Kansas. The northern limits are through the cut-over forests and the poor glacial soils of northern

Michigan and Minnesota. The southern boundary is the hardest to define. A low undulating plateau reaches west from the Appalachian country. It covers most of Kentucky, intrudes into southern Indiana and Illinois, and in Missouri and Arkansas rises to the Ozark Plateau. This hilly country, like the southern Appalachians, was settled early; its forests were cut recklessly and its soils gullied. It is a run-down country on the whole, and parts of it are almost a man-made desert. The effect of this is cumulative; the more enterprising go north to St. Louis, Chicago or Indianapolis. Those least able to remedy the ills of this area remain. This country does not belong to the Mid-West.

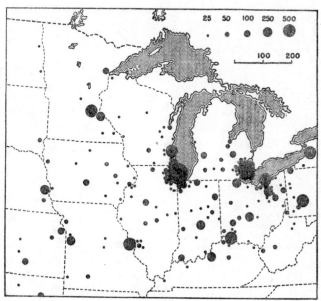

Fig. 23. THE MID-WEST CITIES

THE SETTLEMENT OF THE MID-WEST. The first settlers (see p. 12) came into the Mid-West in the later years of the eighteenth century. They floated down the Ohio, Kentucky and Cumberland Rivers, or came overland from Pittsburgh and Buffalo. There were the exponents of strange religious faiths: the Mennonites, the Amish, the Latter Day Saints; there were the architects of new Utopias, eager to build a para-dise amid the Prairies. The Englishman, Robert Owen, came to New Harmony, in western Indiana, to practise his ideal of communal, socialist living. Miners and prospectors ranged westward. Cornish miners, after the closing down of the copper mines about Redruth, came to northern Illinois, south-western Wisconsin and Upper Michigan where they mined lead, zinc, and copper. Amongst the fanatics were hard-working farmers, wanting only good land to till, and traders looking only for the markets for their wares.

The great immigration was not a disorderly scramble. In 1785 the land survey was begun. Strips of territory were surveyed, six miles across, lying parallel to the western boundary of Pennsylvania. These strips, or "ranges", were divided into "townships", squares of land six miles on each side. Each township was divided into thirty-six sections, each of a square mile, and the sections themselves were divided into

Fig. 24. THE PATTERN OF ROADS IN THE MID-WEST (IOWA AND NEBRASKA)
Note the rectilinear alignment of the roads.

"quarter-sections". The land was sold in units of a section or quarter-section. Generally a quarter-section made up a good sized farm. With a providence that did not often characterize the actions of the early settlers, certain sections were set aside to support the costs of education. Roads were planned to follow the north-south lines between the ranges and the east-west lines between the tiers. These would be supplemented by subsidiary roads built along the section lines. In many parts a road network such as this proved to be redundant, and was left incomplete or, if finished, was allowed to become obsolete. Elsewhere the terrain prevented a too rigid adherence to the pattern laid down by the original surveyors, but across the plains from Ohio to Kansas the nine-

teenth-century surveyors have laid upon the land a pattern of inter-
minable little squares. The system is efficient, stereotyped and monotonous. Figs. 22 and 24 show the road pattern that has grown up in
the Appalachian Ridge-and-Valley, in the hills of Western Pennsylvania and on the level lands of the Mid-West.

Cincinnati was laid out in 1819 by a company of settlers who shared
the strange idea that they were acting in the spirit of the ancient
Roman, Cincinnatus. Indianapolis was founded in 1820; Chicago, in
1833; St. Louis (Mo.), in 1823; and St. Paul and Minneapolis in 1854
and 1856. Cities beyond the Mississippi came later; Kansas City,
Omaha, Council Bluffs were stations on the westward migration routes.
All these cities expanded very rapidly, partly because their sites had
been chosen with especial care; all are route centres, well placed to
serve as market and industrial cities for a large area of rich farmland.
These large cities are described more fully later. Between them there
grew up an even spread of smaller towns, commonly spaced at intervals
of twenty to forty miles, with populations of between 15,000 and 40,000.
They are as unvarying, as monotonous and as inartistic as the square
sections and townships amid which they lie. Each has a town square of
one or two "blocks" each way. In the middle stands the courthouse;
around the square lie the shops, built of brick or stone, with "mock"
fronts, carried high in an attempt to give them dignity. The streets are
straight and parallel to one or other of the sides of the square. The
houses are of wood and separated one from the other by the grass-
covered "yards". In the more humid areas trees are abundant, and the
town can be colourful and picturesque, if not beautiful.

The Mid-West town has usually a manufacturing industry or two:
light or electrical engineering or the production of some type or other
of consumers' goods. It will have a representative of each of the "dime"
stores,[1] and all the larger shops will be chain-stores. There will be the
showrooms of the two leading mail-order firms,[2] the local commercial
broadcasting station, half a dozen cinemas, and a hotel which assumes,
for reasons of prestige, the form of a miniature skyscraper. The traveller
from the East would look in vain for a theatre, bookshop, art gallery,
museum or concert hall, in the English acceptance of these terms.

The Mid-West contains about a quarter of the population of the
United States; it contains the greater part of the wheat, corn, cattle and
dairy production in the United States. It has a considerable share in all
branches of manufacturing industry with the exception of textiles. The

---

[1] i.e. Woolworths and others.
[2] These are Sears, Roebuck and Co. and Montgomery Ward.

Mid-West has a great political importance inside the United States; five out of the last eight presidents have been Middle-Westerners. It is in the small town of the Mid-West that the public opinion of the region is shaped.[1]

THE PHYSICAL SETTING. The Mid-West is a plain, broken by areas of higher and rougher terrain. Most of the region is covered by a deposit of variable thickness of glacial drift, and the topographical features are the products of vicissitudes in its glacial history, rather than of the qualities of the bedrock. On the basis of the differing types of glacial deposit, the Mid-West can be divided into a northern lake region and a southern till plain, which is largely devoid of lakes. The boundary between the two follows a winding course across northern Ohio, Indiana and Illinois, and then north-westwards across Wisconsin and Minnesota.

North of this line the glaciation is more recent than to the south, and the forms of the drumlins and moraines are fresher. The ice spread over this region in a series of lobes, whose centres lay over the area of Green Bay, Lake Michigan, Saginaw Bay and Lake Erie. As it withdrew it laid down a complex series of terminal moraines which enclose these water-bodies. The moraines are not often conspicuous features, but, being composed of coarse material, they are commonly dry whereas the intervening areas were all too often damp and peat-filled. The morainic ridges thus constituted routeways in the early days of settlement, and their alignment helped to locate a number of cities in the northern Mid-West.

The lower ground, between the terminal moraines, is sometimes dotted with drumlins. It is a common sight in northern Illinois or Wisconsin to see the farm-house and barn located atop such a low protuberance for protection from the damp or even from floods. The heavy soil of these depressions produces corn and, towards the north where the summers are too short for corn, a good growth of grass or of fodder crops for the stock. Large areas, especially in Michigan, Wisconsin and Minnesota, are too damp for crop cultivation. Some are undrained bog, in parts of which the cranberry (see p. 69) has been introduced. Some still hold lakes of placid water. Not without reason the motor-cars of Minnesota announce on their number-plates that theirs is the state of "10,000 Lakes". In summer and fall the beauty of some of these lakes

---

[1] It is interesting that the few large cities do not establish the current trends. Chicago, for example, is predominantly Democratic, but is outvoted on party issues by the mainly Republican State of Illinois in which it lies.

almost passes belief. The deep blue of the water contrasts with the paler
blue of the sky, the dark conifers and the varied greens and reds of the
broad-leaved trees.

Amid the tumbled moraines and drumlins are flatter areas, the sites
of lakes during certain phases in the retreat of the ice. Fine sediments
were laid down and now form rich, level farmland. There are patches
of such deposits in Southern Wisconsin and along the shores of Lake
Superior, and an extensive area occupies the valley of the Red River,
on the borders of Minnesota and North Dakota, extending northwards
into the Canadian province of Manitoba. In contrast with these are
the small inliers of bed-rock, which occasionally, like islands, break
the surface of the drift. These are composed of rocks of the greatest
geological age and they display the characteristics of intense ice erosion.
In Wisconsin and extending into the states to west and south, is the so-
called "Driftless Area", which escaped glaciation during the Quaternary period. It is a plateau-like area, deeply dissected by rivers which
discharge to the Mississippi. The roughness of its terrain serves to em-
phasize the role of the ice age in levelling and smoothing the surface
features of the Mid-West.

The more southerly part of the glacial area is lower in altitude and
very much smoother. The moraines are less frequent and generally less
conspicuous; drumlins are fewer, and lakes almost entirely absent.
There are areas of land not naturally well-drained, especially along
the watercourses, but most of the surface is boulder clay capable of
cultivation, and of yielding good crops over much of its area.

Drainage. Almost the whole of the area considered in this chapter
is drained to the Mississippi. The present drainage pattern was initiated
during the retreat of the ice, when a number of rivers developed to
carry the melt-water southwards to the Gulf. The further retreat of the
ice uncovered other outlets for the water escaping from the ice. After
carving out the Mohawk Valley in New York State, it came at last to
pursue its present course by way of the St. Lawrence River to the
Atlantic Ocean. The Mississippi system, though it extends to within a
mile or two of the Great Lakes, does not naturally receive water from
this source. There have, however, been a number of canals cut to link
the Mississippi tributaries with the Great Lakes. Their construction was
eased by the existence of the late glacial river courses, but few of them
served any important economic purpose or became financially profitable. Indeed, only one of them is to-day of importance: the short canal
from Lake Michigan at Chicago to the Illinois River. This has been

formed by linking the Chicago River with the Illinois system and making it flow, as it were, backwards, taking the Lake water south towards the Mississippi. Though of small commercial importance, this additional outlet for the upper Great Lakes is invaluable, as the lake level is tending to rise and threatening to inundate a number of coastal settlements.

The Mississippi, the "Mother of Waters", rises amid the lakes and swamps of northern Minnesota. Below Minneapolis, where the river forms the Falls of St. Anthony, it is incised far below the level of the plateau-like country. This rises above the broad river in a series of high bluffs. The Mississippi quickly becomes a river of impressive width. At Redwing (Minn.) it is over a mile across. Lower down, its course becomes first studded with islands and then broken up into several branches which divide, unite and again divide, enclosing marshy islands and fringed by strips of incultivable marshland. The great river receives the Minnesota, Cedar and Des Moines Rivers from the west; the Wisconsin, Rock and Illinois from the east. Then, a few miles above St. Louis, it is joined by the Missouri and, about 150 miles downstream at Cairo, by the Ohio. Each drains an enormous area; the Missouri, the northern high plains and Rocky Mountains; the Ohio, the Allegheny plateau and most of Indiana, Kentucky and Tennessee.

At Cairo the first few fields of cotton appear; the first cypress trees begin to grow in the river swamps; the number of coloured in the population increases sharply, and we are on the fringes of the South.

The climate of the Mid-West has already been described (pp. 28 to 29), its great extremes and its violent fluctuations, its alternations of tropical warmth with near arctic cold, of violent rainstorms with blizzards. The violence of the climate is reflected in that of the rivers, alternately shallow or even dried up, and raging out of control. Individual rivers may flood at almost any season as the result of excessive local rainfall. When the greater part of the Mississippi system floods it is usually because a thick covering of snow over most of the Mid-West is suddenly melted by warm air masses coming north from the Gulf. An accumulation of snow of many weeks can disappear in as many hours. The run-off is swift, especially in the deforested and eroded hills along the southern limit of the Mid-West. High water moves down the Ohio, the Missouri and their tributaries. In good years the melting is slow, and the high level of one has reached its junction with the Mississippi and been passed on towards the sea before the level in the next has reached its peak. In bad years the floods on each branch are so synchronized that their waters are jostling to enter the main stream of the

Mississippi, pounding one another back and flooding both the valleys of the tributary streams and of the Mississippi itself. The years 1951 and 1952 saw floods of extreme severity: large parts of many Mid-Western cities were under water, with enormous loss both of farm stock and of industrial equipment.

Remedies fall into two groups, the defensive and the preventive. The former consists in building high the banks and levées along the rivers so that they are constrained to keep to their channels. The great banks of stone and earth which line the rivers are crowned with massive walls of reinforced concrete often rising a further 15 or 20 feet. The town of Cairo, at the junction of the Ohio with the Mississippi is like a medieval city surrounded by its fortifications. The concrete levée wall rises high above the streets; openings through it are few and furnished with heavy steel gates which are wedged into place as flood threatens. In summer and autumn the defences of Cairo are as unnecessary as the walls of York or Chester. In winter and spring the inhabitants man the ramparts and are ready with sandbags to repel an enemy stronger and more destructive than any human foe.

The alternative course is to strike at the causes of the floods, the sudden run-off over the whole Mississippi drainage basin. This can be done by establishing a thicker vegetation cover and by building dams along the rivers, which can regulate their discharge. These remedies have hitherto been applied on a large scale only in the Tennessee Valley, but their success here (see p. 88) has led to the proposal to regulate similarly other rivers. First to be considered has been the Missouri. But as the remedial work on the Missouri River lies far out on the western plains it is examined in the next chapter.

AGRICULTURE. The Mid-West is the farming region of the United States *par excellence*. The dominant influences on both soil and crops are the rainfall and humidity, decreasing from east to west, and the length and severity of winter, increasing from south to north. Rainfall in Ohio and southern Indiana is generally over 40 inches a year, and the humidity, except during spells of very cold weather, is high. Under these conditions a grey-brown podzolic soil is produced. Towards the north this passes into the true podzol of the northern parts of Michigan, Wisconsin and Minnesota. In the drier conditions of Illinois, Iowa and southern Minnesota prairie soils are developed. These dark soils, rich in plant food, are intermediate between the rather leached podzolic soils of the east and the black chernozem which lies along the dry western margin of the Mid-West (fig. 8).

The growing period between the last killing frost of spring and the first of autumn is about 200 days along the southern borders of the Mid-West, diminishing to less than 150 in northern Wisconsin and Minnesota. Even in the most southerly parts of the Mid-West the season is too short for the effective growth of cotton, and the economy and society based on cotton cultivation are foreign to the Mid-West.

The distribution of the major crops in the Mid-West, is, in part, a response to these physical influences, in part to transport and market considerations. Four crop regions may be distinguished.

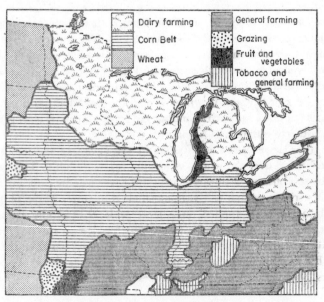

Fig. 25. THE MID-WEST: AGRICULTURAL REGIONS

1. *The Corn Belt.* Largest and in many respects the most important of these is the Corn Belt. It extends from Ohio to Nebraska and from southern Indiana to Minnesota. Throughout this area, a deep, warm soil, rich in organic material, a rainfall well distributed through the growing season, and hot days and warm nights combine to favour corn, a term which in America is restricted to the crop we call maize. Corn, which is exhausting in its demands on the soil and seasonal in its labour requirements, is commonly associated with oats, winter wheat, soya beans and grasses and legumes. The corn that is sown to-day has been evolved from the primitive grain that fed the Indians and early settlers. It is a tall plant, rearing its feathery, pollen-yielding plume 10 or 12

SOUTH CHICAGO STEELWORKS OF THE UNITED STATES STEEL CORPORATION. *On the is Lake Michigan. In the middle distance a Great Lakes iron-ore carrier can be seen alongside of the unloading quays. Immediately behind the ore heaps are the blast furnaces.*
AN OPENCAST IRON-ORE PIT IN THE MESABI RANGE, MINNESOTA.

(I) A FARM NEAR OKLAHOMA CITY. *This is a wheat farm with subsidiary cattle raising*
(II) A DAIRY FARM IN WISCONSIN. *Note the large barn suitable for stall-feeding in winter*

feet from the ground; its leaves are heavy and rich, and the several heavy corn cobs that it bears make it the heaviest yielding of all the grains. The evolution of hybrids has increased the yield and made it more dependable. In addition to *dent* and *flint* corn, generic terms for the varieties most often cultivated, sweet corn is grown for human consumption and *popcorn* has a large market amongst children, in addition to being the invariable accompaniment of a visit to the "movies".[1] Corn is grown in every state of the Union, but only in the Corn Belt is it the dominant crop. In parts of Iowa and Illinois it is grown as a cash crop, but over most of the Corn Belt its cultivation is associated with the fattening of hogs and cattle. The hogs are bred on the corn farms, where they "convert concentrated feeds into meat with a high degree of physical efficiency". The corn cobs are fed to them, and they are allowed to root amongst the bent and withered corn stalks for any that the mechanical corn picker may have missed. Beef cattle commonly take the surplus in these areas. Some cattle are bred outside the Corn Belt in the drier grazing lands of the West, and are brought on to the corn farms for fattening *en route* to the packing centres, but most are reared within the Corn Belt itself.

All the hogs and cattle ultimately make their way to the packing house, where the animals are slaughtered and the carcases dismembered with the utmost expedition and efficiency. Largest and most famous of the packing centres is Chicago, which accounts, however, for less than a tenth of the total hogs slaughtered in the United States. The primacy of Chicago derives from the establishment of such an industry here early in the nineteenth century and from the series of railways which radiate from the city into the Corn Belt. Second in importance to Chicago is St. Louis (Mo.), close to the southern margin of the Corn Belt. Then follow Omaha (Nebr.), St. Paul (Minn.), Kansas City (Mo.) and Sioux City (Ia.).

Towards the western margin of the Corn Belt the corn is replaced by winter wheat, and towards the northern with fodder crops or grass. The limits of the belt are continually changing in response to the shifts in demand for corn and for other agricultural products.

2. *The Dairy Region.* The automobile number-plates, a rough but ready source of geographical information, announce that Wisconsin is "America's Dairyland". Wisconsin leads the United States in the volume of liquid milk, butter and cheese produced, but Minnesota,

[1] Sweet corn has a small sugar content. Popcorn contains a gluten which causes it to "explode" when heated. It is in this condition that it serves as a delicacy.

H

Illinois and Michigan are also very large producers. These states lie partly or wholly within the broken area of more recent glaciation. The terrain is less suited than in the more level Corn Belt to the use of agricultural machines. The dampness of much of the soil is more favourable to grass and fodder than to grain crops, and the summer is too short and sometimes too cool for corn to do well. The better parts of the dairy region are distinguished by their closely spaced farms, each with a tall silo and an enormous barn in which the dairy cattle are stall-fed through much of the winter. Near the large cities much of the

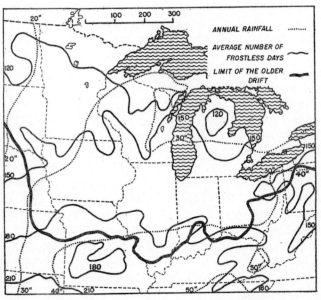

Fig. 26. THE MID-WEST: SOIL, RAINFALL AND THE LIMIT OF THE
QUATERNARY GLACIATION

milk is taken liquid to feed the urban population, but in areas less well served by the means of transport, butter and cheese are made. Wisconsin is particularly noted for the manufacture of cheese which was introduced by Swiss immigrants and is carried on chiefly in small cheese factories by traditional methods. European types of cheese are imitated very successfully.

3. *The Winter Wheat Region.* Wheat was initially a crop less exacting in its climatic requirements than corn, and by selective breeding the range of climate in which it can be grown successfully has been very

greatly increased. Although wheat is grown in greater or less degree over the whole of the Mid-West it is the dominant crop only toward the drier, western margin.

In a large area of Kansas, and over neighbouring parts of Nebraska, Colorado, Oklahoma and northern Texas, a winter wheat is grown. The crop is sown in the autumn and reaped in June or July. The level or rolling land facilitates the use of combine-harvesters; the young plants give some protection to the topsoil against the fierce winds of the Prairies, and wheat is the only important crop that grows well in these areas with less than 25 inches of rainfall a year. Indeed, the cultivation of wheat has been extended deeper into the arid region than is desirable. Towards the western margin of the wheat belt, a crop is taken every other year, and during alternate seasons the soil lies bare to absorb and conserve moisture. This "dry farming" (see p. 134) leaves the top-soil without a plant cover and exposed to the destructive blast of the wind.

The winter wheat is commonly grown alone, sometimes with a periodic fallow. Only in moister areas are supplementary crops, such as oats, barley and sorghums, cultivated. Climate restricts agriculture to one dominant crop; the lack of a rotation over much of the belt is leading to an impoverishment and destruction of the soil.

4. *The Spring Wheat Region.* Wheat is again the dominant crop in western Minnesota and North and South Dakota. Physical conditions are similar, except that the length and severity of the winter greatly restrict the growing period. In consequence, the wheat is sown in spring and reaped in late summer. In the moister areas of the east, especially in the good, lacustrine soils along the valley of the Red River, wheat is grown in rotation with fodder crops and other grains. Towards the west, wheat is the only cultivated crop, and the economic and technical problem arises here, as it does further to the south, of how to diversify the agricultural pattern in this area of low rainfall.

In the early days of the development of the Spring Wheat region the grain was transported by the railroads east to the Mississippi. Minneapolis, the starting point of a number of these lines became a flour-milling centre, a function which it has retained. To-day, however, a great deal of the grain is carried further to the east, either by lake freighter or by rail, to milling centres such as Buffalo. There is also a group of milling centres in the winter wheat belt, at Kansas City, Omaha and St. Louis.

The wheat grown in these two belts is of the hard variety, suitable for bread-making. Along the moist, eastern border of the wheat belts a softer wheat is produced on account of the greater humidity. This is less suited for bread-making; very little of it is exported, and in the United States as a whole its production amounts to less than a quarter of that of the hard wheats.

There are certain small areas of the Mid-West with a highly special-ized production of fruit or of fresh vegetables. An important "trucking" area surrounds Chicago and other large lakeside cities, and temperate fruits are important along the eastern shore of Lake Michigan, where the water moderates somewhat the extremes of climate.

INDUSTRIES OF THE MID-WEST. It must not be supposed that the Mid-West is only a vast region of prosperous agriculture. For a century and a half industries have been spreading into the region, as broad in their nature as the demands of this varied region. In the earliest years of its economic development, the Mid-West sent its agricultural pro-ducts, its skins, hides, wheat and corn-fed farm stock, back east. Early movement was chiefly by water, down the Ohio and Mississippi or by way of the Erie Canal. Then in the 1850's the first railways reached the Ohio and Great Lakes and stretched their fingers into the Mid-West. Their rail-heads and their junctions became the foci of towns and developed manufacturing industries.

Agricultural Industries. The oldest of the industries of the Mid-West are those based on its agricultural products. Flour-milling developed and remains an industry of immense importance at Kansas City, Buffalo and Minneapolis. On the range lands beyond the limits of cultivation cattle were reared, rounded up and driven along the trails to the rail-head at Dodge City, Abilene or Topeka (all in Kansas). From here the animals were shipped to packing stations, where they were slaughtered, dismembered and preserved in smoke, salt, sugar and, later, in tins. One of the earliest Mid-West packing centres was Cincinnati on the Ohio. But more westerly packing centres grew up with the westward movement of the range cattle industry: Chicago, St. Louis, Kansas City. The range gave way to the ranch (see p. 134); the cattle began to make a temporary halt in their eastward progression to the cannery to put on a little weight by feeding for a month or two in the Corn Belt. Hogs, reared and fattened in the same area, joined the movement towards the packing stations. Chicago came to the fore. Its immense stock yards received animals by each of the many railways that radiated from the city; its packing factories prepared the meat, dressed the hides and collected the offal and bones for manufacture into fertilizers. Chicago retains the primacy in this industry; it is in fact impossible to think of Chicago without its stockyards even if the conditions are less colourful and more sanitary to-day than those portrayed over a generation ago in Upton Sinclair's *The Jungle*.

There are other less important food processing industries, the pressing of soya-beans for oil, the making of butter and cheese in the factories in Michigan and Wisconsin, and, on the southern border of the Mid-West, distilling and the preparation of cotton for the market. But it would be far from the truth to assume that those industries associated with the preparation of agricultural products are the most important in the Mid-West to-day. The growth of factory industries has been encouraged by the large and growing market in the Mid-West; by the ease of communications with all other parts of the United States; by the large reserves of fuel, especially coal, and by the existence here of the largest reserves of iron ore in the country. Iron and steel industries, engineering, especially agricultural and automobile, printing, glass and chemical manufactures, and oil refining are all carried on.

Mineral Industries. The coal reserves of the Mid-West are noteworthy rather for their quantity and their wide extent than for their quality. Two fields, known as the Eastern and the Western Interior Coal fields, underlie respectively large parts of Indiana-Illinois and Missouri-Iowa. The coal lies generally in shallow, level seams which are inexpensive to mine. Strip- or opencast-mining has been adopted very extensively where the coal is near enough to the surface. Most of the Mid-West coal is soft and smoky, and has a low heating capacity. There is very little coking coal, and the Mid-West iron-smelting industry is dependent upon Pennsylvania and West Virginia for fuel. Nevertheless, the output from these Mid-Western fields, about a hundred million tons in 1948, is more than sufficient for most other needs of the area.

Many pools of oil still underlie the Mid-West, and are tapped in Ohio, Indiana, Illinois and Kansas, and yield approximately one-tenth of the total United States production. Nowhere in the Mid-West does one see the forest of derricks that mark out the oil-fields of Oklahoma and Texas. Instead one finds, scattered about the fields or along the roadside, small, silent and unobtrusive pumps, operated electrically, with little evidence of the work in hand beyond a small tank to receive the oil.

The Mid-West contains by far the larger part of the iron-ore reserves of the United States. They occur in a series of ranges in Upper Michi-

gan, Wisconsin and Minnesota. Although the volume of ore was originally very great, the intensive exploitation during the past sixty years,
during which this ore-field yielded over two-thirds of the total output
of the continent, has greatly depleted the reserves. Open-cast workings
are now beginning to give place to underground, and plans are being
made to use a lower-grade ore. The Great Lakes ore now being worked
has an average metal content of about 51 per cent. There remain, however, large reserves of a hard, very low-grade ore, known as taconite,
the development of which is dependent upon the introduction of an
effective means of concentrating the poor ore.

The ore-fields lie close to the western and southern shore of Lake
Superior. Ore is shipped from loading points on the shore through
the Great Lakes to consuming centres in the eastern Great Lakes
area. The iron-smelting centres of the Mid-West are intermediate
between the sources of coking coal in western Pennsylvania and West
Virginia and the sources of ore in the upper Great Lakes. The iron
works lie close to the water so that the ore can be unloaded directly
from the boats into the works. A part of the ore brought through the
Great Lakes is carried overland from the Lake Erie ports to the smelting
centres within the Allegheny Plateau.

The transport of ore is seasonal. The Great Lakes freeze for a variable
period during the winter months, and the ore ships normally go into
their winter quarters in November, to emerge again during March.
During the remaining months of the year they work intensively.
Mechanical loading and unloading hastens the turn round of the boats.
Where the lake waters are narrow two steady processions of huge ore-
boats, one loaded, the other in ballast, can be seen stretching to the
horizon. The shipping activity is not less than that in Southampton
Water or the Thames estuary. The approaching exhaustion of the
Great Lakes ore makes it highly necessary not only to discover an alter-
tive source but one for which the vast apparatus of ore-boats and docks
can continue to be used. Such a deposit has been found on the borders
of Quebec and Labrador, but if it is to supply the Mid-West iron industry the improvement of the St. Lawrence waterway (see p. 180) will
be necessary.

The largest concentration of the iron-smelting and steel-making
industries in the Mid-West lies at the head of Lake Michigan, where
Gary is the most important single centre. Steel from these mills is sent
to engineering works throughout the United States. Buffalo and Cleveland are lesser smelting centres but have important steel-using industries. In Detroit the smelting and steel-making industry is tributary to

the automobile industry which dominates the city. Although the motor industry of Detroit owes its origin to the initiative and energy of a few individuals who happened to make their industrial beginnings in the city, the site has considerable advantages. It is well-placed to receive the minerals and other materials it needs; it has the advantage of water transport on the Great Lakes, and it lies in the richest and most densely populated region of the United States.

The manufacture of agricultural equipment and machinery is important in many Mid-Western cities. The chemical industries are carried on at Cleveland, Chicago, St. Louis and at many other centres. Akron (Ohio) is the largest American centre of the rubber industry and produces tyres for the motor cars made in Detroit.

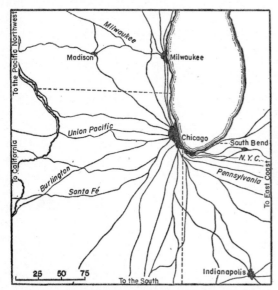

No less than 22 main line railways radiate from the city. Only the more important are shown, and most are indicated by the popular abbreviations of their names: Milwaukee (Chicago, Milwaukee, St. Paul and Pacific R.R.), Burlington (Chicago, Burlington and Quincy R.R.), Santa Fé (Atchison, Topeka and Santa Fé R.R.), N.Y.C. (New York Central R.R.).

Fig. 27. CHICAGO AS A RAILWAY CENTRE

CITIES OF THE MID-WEST. Within the area considered in this chapter are no fewer than eighteen cities of over 100,000 people. It is possible to describe each of only a small group of the larger amongst them.

Chicago. Foremost in every respect is Chicago (3,606,436). The city grew up in the early years of the nineteenth century where the small Chicago River entered Lake Michigan. The lake shore was low and swampy; the site chosen was one of the drier spots in this area. A portage, now replaced by a canal, led from the Chicago to the Des Plaines

River and thus to the Mississippi. Routeways from east to west curved round the head of the lake, and Chicago developed very early as a route centre. It has retained this function, and to-day it focuses a greater number of railway routes than any other traffic centre in the world (see p. 109). Most of Chicago's industries, especially meat packing (see p. 106), derive from the excellence of communications. The greater Chicago area is an important centre of the iron and steel, automobile and engineering industries, and its excellent railroad and road communications have made it by far the most important warehousing and distributing centre in the Mid-West. Despite its lakeside position, Chicago is not an important port. In fact, the only commodity regularly handled by lake freighter is the iron ore bound for Gary and South Chicago. Chicago is essentially a focus of land, not of lake communications.

Chicago is a colourful, cosmopolitan city with a variety that it is difficult to describe. In it many immigrant groups live, as they tend also to do in New York, in compact communities in which the traditions of each are in some way preserved: the Irish, Czech, German and other "quarters" (see fig. 28). It is a city with an international outlook, but contains the most well-known section of the "isolationist" press. The rich area along the "gold coast" north of the city possibly contains more wealthy people than any similar area elsewhere on the globe, yet it would be hard indeed to find the equal of the slums of some parts of the coloured quarter. A magnificent promenade and driveway run along the lake shore for about fifteen miles, backed by parks and the tall buildings of the city. A fresh breeze blows off the lake,

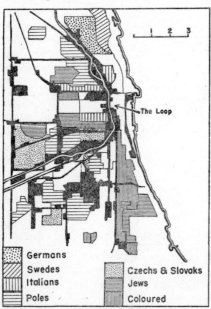

Germans
Swedes
Italians
Poles

Czechs & Slovaks
Jews
Coloured

Fig. 28.
THE "ETHNIC" REGIONS OF CHICAGO
(*after Maurice Halbswachs*)
This map was published in 1934. The limits of certain residential districts, especially that of the "coloured", have changed slightly since that date. The black areas on the map are factories, railways and marshalling yards.

justifying the name of the "windy city" by which Chicago is known to Americans. Chicago is well known for its museums, libraries and art galleries as it is for the activities of the underworld, whose shadow still hangs over some parts of the city.

Milwaukee (632,651) lies only 90 miles north of Chicago, on the western shore of Lake Michigan. It is overshadowed by its great neighbour, but is nevertheless an important industrial city. Its engineering and automobile industries draw materials from the north-eastern industrial region of the United States, and its products are distributed westwards through Wisconsin, Minnesota and Iowa. Milwaukee was from the first a predominantly German settlement, and German is still spoken by some of its inhabitants. This has something to do with the fact that Milwaukee is famous as a brewing centre.

Detroit (1,838, 517) is second in size only to Chicago in the Mid-West. It was, as its name suggests, in origin a French settlement established on the "narrows" of the St. Clair River as it flows from Lake Huron to Lake Erie. It became a starting point for immigrants moving westwards across Michigan, then a supply point for the settlers. From the first its people were interested in transport, and here Henry Ford developed the mass production of automobiles. Detroit is well placed both to receive the raw materials of its industry and also to distribute its products to the American market. In Detroit to-day are the chief works of the three large automobile concerns[1] as well as of several smaller, and its industries include the production of glass, paint, rubber and non-ferrous metals, all tributary to the motor industry.

Cleveland (905,636) lies only 90 miles away from Detroit, across Lake Erie. It shares with Gary and Detroit the advantages of lying between the sources of iron ore and of coking coal and of having water transport for the former. Cleveland is the greatest of the Great Lake ports. It has developed steel and non-ferrous metal industries and is in many ways a commercial capital for the many smaller industrial centres which extend eastwards and southwards towards the Pennsylvania border.

Cincinnati (500,510), on the Ohio River, and Indianapolis (424,683) in the midst of the plains of Indiana, grew up as business and industrial centres on the routes leading west. To-day they have varied engineering

[1] General Motors, Chrysler, Ford; the smaller companies are Hudson and Packard. The Studebaker works are at South Bend (Ind.) and Nash at Kenosha, near Milwaukee (Wis.). The Hudson and Nash corporations have recently (1954) amalgamated to form "American Motors".

and food processing industries and each serves as commercial centre for a large area of the Mid-West.

Minneapolis and St. Paul. The twin cities of Minneapolis (517,277) and St. Paul (309,474) make up the most northerly urban concentration of the Mid-West. The two cities lie on opposite banks of the Mississippi, though their centres are no less than ten miles apart. St. Paul, lowermost on the river, is the effective limit of navigation on the Mississippi, and owed its early growth to this fact. Minneapolis grew up at the Falls of St. Anthony. When wheat growing developed on the plains of the Red River Valley, the grain was shipped eastwards to the river. The growth of milling industries was encouraged by the availability of water power, and, though the falls have long since ceased to suffice for this purpose, flour milling remains an important industry. To it have been added in both Minneapolis and St. Paul a variety of engineering and consumers' goods industries.

St. Louis (852,623) grew up on the high western bank of the Mississippi a few miles below the junction of the Missouri. It commanded the westward route which crossed the southern border of the plains of the Mid-West, and ascended the Missouri River and at the same time controlled the traffic of the Mississippi. The river traffic southwards to the Gulf, so important in the early nineteenth century, has now been tapped by the east to west railways, and transport is not now of great importance. Nevertheless, the great significance of St. Louis as a route centre remains, and has attracted to this area a wide range of manufacturing industries from flour milling and meat packing to steel, glass and clothing.

To this list of cities should be added many others: Toledo (301,358), the railway and steel town at the western end of Lake Erie; Columbus (374,770) in central Ohio; Akron, Ohio (273,189), centre of the rubber industry; Louisville, Ky. (367,359), an Ohio river port and industrial city; Fort Wayne, Ind. (132,840), South Bend, Ind. (115,698); Peoria Ill., (111,523); Evansville, Ind. (109,869); Madison, Wis. (95,594). Scattered between these large cities is an immense number of smaller, forming an increasingly open pattern as the dry western limit of the Mid-West is approached.

— 9 —

The South

T HE American South is, in the words of C. O. Sauer, "a major
cultural division of the United States, perhaps its most strikingly
outstanding cultural unit".[1] It is one that is on the whole well
appreciated in the United Kingdom. Its individuality springs in the
main from its climate. Over large areas of the South sub-tropical crops
—cotton, rice, sugar—will grow; field labour in the heat of the summer
is hard for white people, and negro slaves began to be imported early in
the seventeenth century. Thus an aristocratic society developed, based
on slave-run plantations and the export of plantation crops. In England, a sentimental affection for the Old South rested on the sound
economic basis of the exchange of English factory and quality goods for
the raw cotton of the southern states. Sentimental ballads and romantic
novels have combined to give a colourful if not always correct picture
of the American South.

PHYSICAL GEOGRAPHY. The South, like New England and the
Mid-West, is rather a cultural and economic than a physical province.
In terms of physical geography it is very varied indeed. It is made up
of a coastal plain which stretches all the way from the Chesapeake Bay
to the Mexican border. Inland of this is a region of rolling hills from
which rise, in the southern Appalachians and in the Ozark and
Ouachita Plateaux, mountains of considerable height.

The coastal plain wraps around the southern extremity of the Appalachian Mountains and their Piedmont plateaux (see fig. 29). It is low and
undulating; its dominant relief features lie in a series of arcs around the
southern extension of the mountains. These consist of a series of low
scarps formed in limestone or sandstone and separated by depressions
of which some are floored with softer rock. Towards the outer margin of

[1] Carl O. Sauer, *Geography of the Pennyroyal* (Frankfort, Ky., 1927), p. 5.

113

the plain these beds dip beneath soft deposits of Tertiary and more recent date.

The lower valley of the Mississippi River occupies a structural depression between the Appalachians to the east and a similar though less conspicuous uplift, the Ozark and Ouachita Mountains, to the west. From the frontiers of the Mid-West, in southern Illinois, southwards to the sea, the great river is bordered by a wide alluvial tract, some of it drained and under cultivation, much still in the condition of swamp. West of the river a similar series of scarps, formed by the very gently dipping beds, loops around the Ouachita Mountains and then stretches westward into the high plains (see Chapter 10) which border the Rocky Mountains.

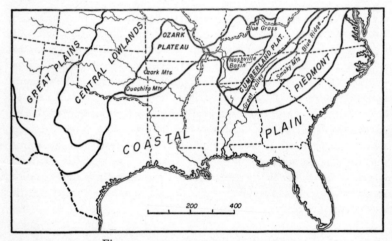

Fig. 29. THE SOUTH: RELIEF REGIONS

The Appalachian Mountains have already been described. As they continue southwards they become broader and higher, culminating in the Blue Ridge and Great Smoky Mountains of North Carolina. Then, abruptly, they sink into the Piedmont and are lost.

Most of the characteristics of life in the South derive from its climate. As a whole the region experiences long and hot summers and short, mild winters. The whole of the South has an average temperature above freezing in January, and at least half of the area is above 45 degrees. The summer temperatures are more uniform, with July averages a little above or below 80 degrees. The frost-free period ranges from about 200 days in the north to the whole year in Florida and along the Gulf coast. Most of the South has a rainfall of over 50 inches in the

year. This diminishes slowly towards the north and more sharply westwards. The moderate rainfall of eastern Texas changes to near desert
conditions in western.

The enervating heat of the summer of much of the South, combined
with its high humidity, saps the strength and produces a lassitude that
makes any effort a burden. Labour in the fields was regarded from the
earliest days of European settlement as difficult for white men. Inden-
tured white labourers, and after them negroes from West Africa, were
brought in and they cultivated the rice and tobacco, cut the sugar cane
and picked the cotton. The slave society of the South found its strongest
sanction in the southern climate.

Continuously high temperatures over much of the South, combined
with a heavy rainfall, have reduced the soils in many parts almost to
the condition of laterite. Humus remains in the soil for only a short
time. Many chemical constituents of the soil decompose, and are removed in solution, until only a clay richly impregnated with insoluble
iron salts remains. Over much of the South the soil section exposed in
gullies and on road cuttings is a deep red or orange in colour, beautiful,
if it had not its own tale of poverty to tell. There are, however, exceptions. In parts of Alabama, Mississippi and Texas belts of soft limestone
support a clay soil. This is retentive of humus and is dark, even black,
when turned up by the plough. These black belts contain the areas of
the most intensive cotton growing.

Along all the great valleys is a belt of alluvial soil, laid down by
the rivers and continuously renewed by their floods. Greatest of these is
the alluvial plain of the Mississippi which stretches from Cairo to the
sea, a tract over 500 miles in length and from 30 to 120 miles in width.
When cleared of swamp forest and drained, the alluvial tracts offer one
of the richest soils of the South.

In several areas of the South, especially North Carolina, Florida and
Louisiana, depressions in the land surface have filled with peat and to-
day form swamp or marsh.

The vegetation of the South springs from its soil and climate. When
the white man entered the region, it was almost continuously forested.
Over the highlands was a cover of hardwood—oak and hickory—forest,
with occasionally pines on the poorer soil and at greater heights. The
whole Piedmont was a mixed oak and pine forest, while the coastal
plain, from North Carolina to Texas, was a spreading forest of long-leaf,
slash and loblolly pines. The "piney woods" of the South occupied the
poorest of the lateritic soils where they had supplanted the broad-
leaved trees.

In American parlance a swamp is a marsh with trees. Along the alluvial tracts of all the rivers, were swamps, where the cypress, tupelo and swamp cottonwood rose from the stagnant waters. Much of the swamp has been cleared and the land brought under cultivation, but still along the Mississippi, in the Great Dismal of North Carolina, the Okefinokee of South Carolina and in smaller areas in Florida, Mississippi and Louisiana, the fetid swamps remain, the trees rising as if on stilts from the slime. Between their "knees" and amidst the stiff sawgrass are alligators and water mocassins, as venomous as they are small, and insects of every colour and size; and, in the tree-tops, myriads of brightly coloured birds. In places the trees disappear, giving place to

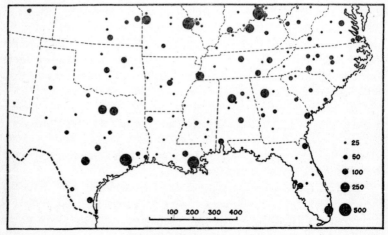

Fig. 30. THE SOUTH: CITIES

tall marsh grass as in the Everglades and along the Louisiana coast. Around the coasts of southern Florida, on the border of the humid tropics, is a girdle of mangrove swamp between the Everglades and the sea.

SETTLEMENT AND POPULATION. The earliest settlements of white men were made in the sixteenth century along the Atlantic coast. The mission stations of the Spaniards in Florida and the English settlements along the James River in Virginia were the earliest. Then settlers spread southwards through the coastal plain of the Carolinas and inland to the Piedmont. Slaves, caught in West Africa and landed on the quays of Charleston and Savannah, provided labour. Rice, grown in the swamps along the rivers, and sugar formed the economic basis of a planter society. As settlers spread on to the drier soils of the Piedmont, rice declined in importance and cotton and tobacco gained. Until the end of the eighteenth century little cotton was grown outside the Piedmont region of North and South Carolina. Then, almost simultaneously a technological revolution in the European textile industry, the invention in America of the cotton gin, essential if short-staple cotton was to be grown (see p. 12), and the removal of Indian tribes, which had blocked advance along the southern Piedmont, created both a demand for cotton and the opportunity to supply it.

In the first twenty years of the nineteenth century the cotton fields spread through the "piney woods" of Alabama and became established on the rich bottom lands of the Mississippi. On the eve of the American Civil War, cotton was king throughout the South. From the Carolinas to Texas it was the chief crop. The distribution of slaves accorded almost exactly with that of cotton growing. The stately houses of the plantation owners, which owed something both in their architecture and in the leisured, sophisticated lives of their owners, to the aristocracy of eighteenth-century England, spread through the South.[1]

New Orleans, established by French settlers about 1718, was the source from which spread another wave of settlers northwards into the alluvial plains of the Mississippi. Here French planters grew fine cotton on the rich soil and built stately mansions, which remain to-day, along the banks of the river.

As the cotton kingdom spread westwards, the southward-flowing rivers were used more and more to carry the cotton bales down to the sea. The Mississippi, artery of the most important cotton growing area, became a great highway. The flat-boat, propelled only by the current of this wayward river, gave way to the paddle-steamer and the stern-wheeler, whose soaring decks were piled high with cotton bales.

Yet a third stream of settlers entered the South, very different from those who had carried the plantation system westwards to Louisiana and Texas. These were the humbler folk who had moved through the Appalachian valleys and had issued through the gaps in the Cumberland Plateau (see p. 88) on to the low plateaux of Kentucky and Tennessee. Here they settled the better soils of the Blue Grass and the Nashville Basin. Some passed on through the hills of southern Indiana and southern Illinois into the plateaux and mountains of the Ozark and Ouachita. Their society and economy were different from those of the cotton planters. Cotton would not grow successfully so far north.

---

[1] The reader will remember the romantic, nostalgic picture of southern society before the Civil War which was drawn by Margaret Mitchell in *Gone with the Wind*.

Winter was long enough to produce a lull in the round of farm activities, and slaves were not much wanted when there was little to employ them for part of the year. Few of the rivers were navigable, and the rough terrain made transport difficult. Early society was very nearly self-sufficient. The diet of corn and hog flesh, and the garments of leather and home-spun, could be produced on the farm. Self-sufficient also was their culture (see p. 87). Without the fertilizing ideas and influences of the outer world, it remained narrow and primitive. The Ozark highlands to the west mirrored faithfully the intellectual growth of the highlands of Kentucky and Tennessee and have also become a reservoir of folk-songs and folk-lore.

The old southern society was destroyed and the development of the southern economy checked for a generation by the American Civil War of 1861–5, known to every southerner as the "War between the States". Memories of this war and of the long period of northern domination that followed it have left an ineradicable impression on the South. Even if to-day there are perceptible cracks in the political uniformity of the "solid" South, the region is, on the whole Democrat in the face of the predominantly Republican north-east. In all southern states there is in some degree a colour bar. White and coloured are segregated in the schools and colleges;[1] "jim-crow" laws require the coloured population to take inferior seats on the trains and street cars. Even in the nation's capital, which is enclosed by the marginal state of Maryland, negroes are not admitted to some theatres and are not served in certain restaurants. In the "deep South", in Mississippi, there are towns where negroes do not dare to exercise their legal right of voting at the polls. Throughout the South the negro is in effect a "second-class citizen".

The South is to-day undergoing an economic revolution (see p. 123) and is rapidly making good the lost years of the nineteenth century. But still the "Old South" focuses loyalties as it did almost a century ago. The flag of the southern states is flown on all possible occasions and the southerners sing "Dixie" as if it were their own national anthem.

Southern society was rural. The only large city a century ago was the port of New Orleans. All other cities were small, and owed their existence to their function as coastal and river ports. The development of cities has been very largely the achievement of the present century. The map, fig. 30, shows the distribution of cities in the South in 1950, and fig. 31 shows for comparison those of fifty years earlier. This ex-

[1] This particular instance of segregation was declared to be unconstitutional by the Supreme Court in May 1954, but this judgment does not mean the end of segregation.

WHEAT COUNTRY: (I) GRAIN ELEVATORS IN THE WHEAT-GROWING AREA OF NORTHERN TEXAS. *The photograph was taken near Amarillo, Texas.* (II) WHEAT HARVESTING IN THE WINTER WHEAT BELT, *showing self-propelled combine harvesters.*

(I) MINING SETTLEMENT IN THE MOUNTAINS OF SOUTH-WESTERN COLORADO.
(II) SNAKE RIVER VALLEY, ON THE BORDERS OF WYOMING AND IDAHO. *The photogra shows the small, mixed farms, typical of the mountain valleys of this area,*

tremely rapid development is associated especially with the growing
industrialization of the South (see p. 123) and the rise of important
mineral industries in Louisiana, Texas and Oklahoma. In the coastal
regions it is due to the expansion of trade in the staple products of the
South and to the growth of a tourist industry.

On the eve of the Civil War, there were about 4,000,000 negro slaves
in the southern states. By 1950, the number of those classified as
"coloured" had risen to 10,000,000, though in recent years they have
formed a diminishing proportion of the total population, as coloured
move out of the South and find employment elsewhere. In general it
may be said that the more numerous is the coloured population, the
stronger are the legal and extra-legal restrictions on their activities. The
states with the largest coloured populations are in general the poorest

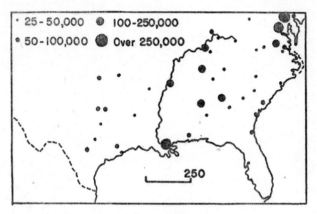

Fig. 31. THE CITIES OF THE SOUTH IN 1910

in the nation. The poverty of the South has had two somewhat contra-
dictory results. On the one hand the low level of education and welfare
has led the more enterprising of the coloured population to move to the
northern or western states, where wages are higher and race prejudice
less pronounced; on the other, the very cheapness of negro labour in the
South is itself attracting industry to the area, thus raising wages and
improving the conditions of the people.

Beside the negro is the "poor white", an inevitable product of a
plural society such as has developed in the South. Depressed members
of the upper, or white, stratum of society are assimilated to the level of
the coloured. In economic status they are not unlike the mountaineers
of Kentucky or Tennessee, but they suffer more by comparison with
the more fortunate members of their own race. The poverty of both

I

the negro and the poor white increases their liability to the diseases normal in a humid sub-tropical climate. Malaria is endemic in some parts; hookworm remains a scourge, with a consequent lowering of human vitality. Nor can human diet be regarded as the best suited to the physical conditions. The South has more than its share of delicacies; the rich can fare very well, but for the poor of both races the traditional diet of corn bread and pork has not everywhere yielded place to something more nutritive and better balanced.

AGRICULTURAL CONDITIONS. In few parts of the South is there a soil of high fertility. Most soils are leached and easily eroded. The traditional patterns of agriculture have not been well adjusted to the physi-

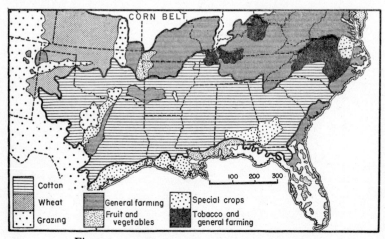

Fig. 32. THE SOUTH: AGRICULTURAL REGIONS

cal conditions. Cotton and tobacco are exhausting crops, and the need for fertilizer is great. They are also particularly vulnerable to plant disease and insect pest. Of all the crops that could be grown in the South, cotton has, through a series of historical and economic circumstances, come to be the dominant one. Almost the whole of the American cotton crop is grown between North Carolina and Texas, and the American crop amounts to almost 50 per cent of the total world production. The heavy labour requirements of cotton encouraged slavery; now the abundance of cheap labour tends to retain cotton as the dominant crop.

While much of the cotton comes from large farms, with adequate capital and efficient management, a considerable amount is produced

by cash tenants or share-croppers, whose rent takes the form of a proportion of their product. Most of the cotton farms are small, and many
have far too little equipment. All too often the traveller sees the tumble-
down shack of the cropper lying amid its small fields, which are cultivated with a mule-drawn plough (the horse is not efficient in the humid
heat), the crop being picked by the combined effort of the family. Over
to the west, in Texas, where the legacy of slavery days hangs less
heavily, fields and farms are larger. Both here and on the large farms
through the South tractors are used for ploughing, and the cotton-
picking machines move slowly through the fields in August, drawing
the white cotton balls on to their revolving drums.

Cotton is a quick growing crop. It is sown about April. By July the
green boll has formed and by August the boll has opened to expose the
tuft of white fibre. The bolls do not open all together, and picking is
spread out over a period of months. But by the end of October the last
is picked in Louisiana and Mississippi. Further north, the prospect of
an early frost has compelled the farmer to finish his harvest much
earlier.

Scattered through the cotton belt are the small gineries where the
seeds are removed from the fibre. The seeds go to oil-seed mills to be
pressed; the cotton fibre is compressed into 500 pound bales and sent
either to the domestic cotton mills or to the cotton ports: Mobile, New
Orleans, Galveston.

Within the cotton belt four areas of production stand out: the Piedmont of South Carolina and Georgia, the black belt of Alabama, the
Mississippi bottom lands and the black prairie of Texas. But cotton-
growing has spread in recent years far beyond the limits of the old
South; into the dry lands of Oklahoma and western Texas, and into the
irrigated valleys along the Mexican border and in New Mexico, Arizona and California.

In the early years of this century, cotton cultivation received a disastrous setback from the depredations of the boll weevil, an insect pest
that spread into the South from Mexico. The westward trend of cotton-
growing has been inspired in part by the need to escape the insect,
which flourishes less in the drier climates.

Corn is the second crop throughout the cotton belt. It is both animal
fodder and human food. The tenant farmer grows little else, and his
land suffers from the overlong concentration on so few crops. A more
diversified agriculture is needed both to improve the soil, to diversify
the diet and also to reduce the sometimes catastrophic degree of dependence upon a single crop.

Animal husbandry was formerly of slight importance. Hogs and chickens were reared, but the maintenance of beef and dairy herds was discouraged by their liability to Texas fever, and by the inadequacy of the native southern grasses for pasture and hay. The eradication of the tick, carrier of the fever, the introduction of fodder crops, and, lastly, the cross-breeding of the native cattle, mostly of English origin, with the Asiatic Bramah strain, are together going far to relieve the problem. There is now a cattle industry in the South, and even dairy farming is of growing importance.

On the borders of the cotton belt are a number of other specialized crops. Along the Atlantic seaboard, and profiting from the developed transport net, is a region where "truck farming" (i.e. market gardening) is important. Early vegetables gathered by itinerant workers— mostly coloured—who move northwards with the season, are grown for the markets of the northern cities.

Northern Florida is the most important area for the cultivation of citrus fruits. Considerably over half the United States orange crop and nearly three-quarters of the grape-fruit are grown in the state, together with small quantities of lemons, tangerines and limes. Even in Florida frost is a danger to the crop. The occasional cold air mass from the north plays havoc in the citrus groves, and always in winter the growers are ready with their "smog-pots" to put a blanket of smoke about the trees. The fruit-growing area of Florida includes also pineapples, peaches and winter strawberries.

In the flat alluvial lands of coastal Louisiana rice is grown in fields flooded with water from the rivers. This cultivation bears no relationship to the slave-run paddy fields of the Carolinas. It is a modern and entirely mechanized industry conducted on large farms. The same area is important for the cultivation of the sugar cane. This lies very close to the climatic margin for sugar; the frost hazard is considerable, and only a high protective tariff makes its cultivation practicable.

Wheat, of slight importance throughout the cotton belt, becomes important amongst the hills and plateaux which form the northern margin of the South. In some parts an almost self-sufficing agriculture is still practised (see p. 87). In others mixed-farming, based on wheat, corn, tobacco and livestock, is practised. Tobacco is the chief cash crop. It is grown in small patches on most farms, and the leaves are hung to dry in the wooden tobacco barns which are so familiar a sight throughout the region.

Forestry remains a very important industry. The South is one of the chief sources in the United States of softwood lumber. There are now

many saw- and pulp-mills, and paper manufacture is becoming a significant industry.

MINERAL RESOURCES. The South is not well endowed. Its only
important deposits of coal and iron ore have already been described
(p. 93). Florida is an important source of phosphate rock, which is
quarried from large deposits in the northern part of the state. From
close to the Mississippi delta a belt of oil-bearing rocks stretches westwards, through Louisiana and Texas and extends southwards beneath
the Gulf of Mexico. It is on this account that the State of Texas has
enlarged its borders to include an appreciable area of sea. The oil industry is discussed in the next chapter. Associated with the mineral oil
are deposits of rock salt and sulphur which each contribute a large part
of the American production.

MODERN INDUSTRY. Industry has been drawn to the South in a
spectacular fashion in recent years. No doubt this is due to some extent
to the attraction of cheap labour and cheap industrial sites. Some industries, especially cotton textiles and certain branches of the chemical
industry, may have come south in order to be close to their sources of
raw materials. But over and above these is the permanent advantage
that the material condition of the South is improving and its market
expanding.

Foremost amongst the new industries is the manufacture of cotton
textiles. Cotton mills are now spread through the Piedmont of North
and South Carolina and of Georgia. The South to-day has 75 per cent
of the cotton spindles in the United States and consumes 92 per cent
of the raw cotton used. The synthetic textiles have followed closely in
the wake of the natural. South Carolina is now the manufacturing
centre for a number of the new fibres that are rivalling cotton and
silk for many uses. Other branches of the chemical industry, besides
the manufacture of rayon and orlon, have been established in the
South. Some are based on the South's resources in sulphur, oil and
natural gas, salt and other minerals. Atomic energy research and
development plants have been built in Kentucky, Tennessee and South
Carolina.

REGIONS OF THE SOUTH. For purposes of description the South is
divided into a number of distinct units, more on the basis of human
adaptation to resources than of physical features.

1. *The Region of Interior Highlands and Plateaux.* This is an irregular tract of plateau extending westwards, though at a lower level, from the Cumberland Plateau towards the Mississippi. It includes within its embrace the Tennessee, Cumberland and Ohio Rivers and it sends a bold salient northwards into Indiana. It narrows as it approaches the Mississippi; it gives rise to the hills of southern Illinois, and expands through Missouri and Arkansas, and dies away into the great plains in Oklahoma.

The whole region lies south of the glacial margin. It is built up of beds of secondary geological age, strongly folded locally and giving rise to marked scarp forms. East of the Mississippi the prevailing surface rock is a cherty limestone, which yields an infertile soil. In two areas, the Blue Grass region and the Nashville basin, erosion has removed these beds and exposed a lower series, which has given rise to a more fertile region, now surrounded by the inward-facing scarps of the newer limestone. These fertile basins contrast with the poor country around them, severely eroded, exhausted by generations of tobacco growing, with small run-down farms, poor roads and all the signs of rural poverty. The Blue Grass and Nashville basins are regions of early and continuous settlement, large and opulent farmhouses and efficient and scientific agriculture. One is conscious that these regions have felt the fostering care of a rural aristocracy, such as that which has left its mark on Virginia and the Carolinas. The Blue Grass shows in its horse rearing and race-horse training something of this ancestry. It is a trim and well-kept landscape, in contrast with the shaggy wilderness that envelops it. White palings, enclosing the farms and race-horse paddocks, and well-built farms and stables, remind the traveller more of Newmarket Heath than the Mid-West.

There are few cities in this region. Louisville (369,129), on its northern edge, grew up as a river port on the Ohio, a service which it still performs. Nashville (174,307) is the urban centre of the Nashville Basin.

West of the Mississippi River this belt of country expands into the Ozark Plateau. This is higher, more dissected, poorer and less populous than the plateaux of Kentucky and Tennessee. To the east, in the St. Francis Mountains, and to the south, in the Boston Mountains, the Ozarks culminate in a rugged terrain which resembles the Cumberland Plateau of Tennessee. South of the Boston Mountains, and separated from them by the deep valley of the Arkansas River, are the Ouachita Mountains, where strongly folded beds have been eroded to form a series of east to west mountain ridges.

The plateaux west of the Mississippi were settled in the first half of the nineteenth century mostly by immigrants who had moved on from Kentucky and Tennessee. The Ozark settlers have the same characteristics as those of the more easterly plateaux (see p. 88). Poor and simple, lacking both education and initiative, they have too often been an object of ridicule or the subject of smug condescension from the more northerly states. To-day the Ozarks are developing as a fruit-growing area and are exporting canned fruit juices to other parts of the states. The western edge of the Ozark Plateau, about Joplin City, is a highly important non-ferrous mining area, and produces in the so-called "Tri-State" district[1] about a third of the United States production of lead and over a tenth of its zinc.

2. *The Piedmont.* This region, as we have seen, wraps around the eastern and southern margins of the Appalachian highlands. Its geological structure is complex, but it has been planated and to-day forms a rolling, sometimes hilly, region, from which rise isolated mountains or monadnocks, outliers of the highlands which lie to the west. The Piedmont slopes to the east from a height of considerably above 1000 feet along its inner, to a bare 500 feet at its outer margin. Its residual soils are of no high fertility though much better than those of the coastal plain. The Piedmont has been too long under cultivation; tobacco in the north, cotton in the south and corn everywhere have taken their toll. To-day abandoned farms and gullied hillsides witness to the poor methods of share-cropper and tenant farmer.

The importance of the Piedmont to-day lies in its growing factory industries. All the way from Virginia to Alabama, the landscape is dotted with new textile mills and chemical plants. The many rivers are dammed for water power, and cables carry the power to scattered factories. Along the eastern edge of the Piedmont, where rapids on the rivers checked navigation and offered a source of power, there grew up a line of towns: Richmond, Va. (230,310); Raleigh, N.C. (65,679); Columbia, S.C. (86,914); Augusta (71,508); Macon (70,252) and Columbus, Ga. (79,611); and Montgomery, Ala. (106,525). All have grown during the present century to become industrial cities of considerable importance. Back on the Piedmont, many other cities have grown to size and importance, largely on the basis of the newly established industries: Roanoke, Va. (91,921); Durham (71,311); Greensboro (74,389); Winston-Salem (87,811) and Charlotte, N.C. (134,042); Greenville, S.C. (58,171); and Atlanta, Ga. (331,314).

[1] The area of the western Ozarks which lies partly in each of the States of Kansas, Oklahoma and Missouri.

3. *The Coastal Plain.* The Atlantic coast has sunk relative to the sea in recent geological times. This has drowned the lower courses of many of the rivers and led to the formation of vast areas of swamp. The currents of the ocean have smoothed out the coastline, forming banks of sand and shingle and lines of low sandy islands such as those that form Cape Hatteras and Cape Fear. Behind the beaches and dunes lies swamp, an obstacle to movement and settlement and a source of disease.

Above the swamp level the soils are poor and leached, as witnessed by their natural vegetation cover of pines. Nevertheless the suitability of the climate for vegetables and fruit, combined with the excellence of the system of transport, have made this a foremost region for the production of perishable goods for the city markets. The region is one of the heaviest consumers of fertilizers on its leached soils.

Cotton remains the most important single crop, much of it grown on small tenant holdings. A little tobacco and a great deal of corn make up the greater part of the crop area. A change is long overdue. To-day much of the land is being grassed down, and stock-rearing, especially of beef cattle, is gaining rapidly in importance.

The many coastal inlets have facilitated the growth of ports. Hampton Roads, at the mouth of the James River (Va.), has provided harbour facilities, not only for the port and naval base of Newport News (42,358) but also for the coal port of Norfolk (213,513), linked by rail with the mines of West Virginia.

The decline of the export trade in cotton from the south-eastern states has brought with it that of many coastal ports. Only Charleston, S.C. (70,174) and Savannah, Ga. (119,638), on the Atlantic coast; and Pensacola, Fa. (43,479) and Mobile, Ala. (129,009) have retained any considerable commercial importance. Both Charleston and Savannah are interesting survivals from the colonial period.

West of the Mississippi, the swampy coastlands continue into Texas. But the climate becomes drier. Cotton is still king, but wears his crown with a difference. The small tenant with his mule is replaced by the large-scale farmer, with his machines and scientific management. The Old South never went beyond Louisiana.

4. *The Mississippi Valley.* This is the vast belt of alluvium which begins at Cairo (see p. 101) and stretches southwards 600 miles to the sea. The width of the belt of alluvium, the hundreds of cut-offs, the huge stagnant branch of the river, the Yazoo, all witness to the great extent and rapidity of its changes and to the violence of its floods. The river

is a vast expanse of water, "the great Mississippi, the majestic, the magnificent Mississippi, rolling its mile-wide tide along, shining in the sun; the dense forest away on the other side; the 'point' above the town, and the 'point' below the town, bounding the river glimpse and turning it into a sort of sea and withal a very still and brilliant and lonely one".[1] The winter storms of the Ohio and Tennessee, the melting snows of the Missouri, and the summer thunderstorms of the prairie rivers all come down to the Mississippi. The river always flooded. De Soto's men in 1543 described an enormous flood that put the whole valley bottom under water. A beginning was made, with the building of levées, to hold the river within its bed, in 1717. At intervals in the eighteenth and all through the nineteenth, levée building went on, until banks of earth ran without a break, except where tributaries came in, all the way from St. Louis to the furthest limits of the delta. And the levées, never high enough to meet the demands of every combination of weather in the river's basin, have continued to be heightened and strengthened. Now, crowned with walls of concrete, they seem proof against floods as great as any that have occurred in the past.

Along the banks of the river are cities which grew to wealth and fame when they served as ports for the cotton that was shipped downstream to the mouth. Memphis (396,000), the dominant city of western Tennessee; Vicksburg (27,948) and Natchez, Miss. (22,740), both on bluffs where higher ground comes close to the river; Baton Rouge, La. (125,629) and New Orleans itself.

New Orleans, La. (570,445), is the oldest settlement and greatest port in the region. Established by the French about 1718 between the river and the deltaic Lake Pontchartrain, it quickly established its commercial supremacy. French settlers spread up the river and through the "bayous" of the Louisiana coast, but always regarded New Orleans as their local capital. The wealth and importance of the old city is reflected still in the style of the city. Like Boston it has still an atmosphere which it derives from the buildings and institutions of the past. Like Cairo the city has to be protected by levées. Most of the city is permanently below the river level. The supply of fresh water and the disposal of sewage are matters of great difficulty. Even the dead are "buried" in vaults above ground.

The delta, shaped like the foot of a bird, is continuously building forward into the Gulf of Mexico. The "passes" have to be dredged and buoyed. Back from the river is a maze of shallow channels threading through the swamps, of islands and "bayous", where still are to be

[1] Mark Twain, *Life on the Mississippi.*

found small groups of French-speaking settlers. Here and there, amid
the swamp, one finds the tall mast of an oil drill or the surface installations of a salt mine or sulphur well; then rice-fields, which look like
those of the Orient until a combine-harvester appears to harvest the
grain, and sugar plantations like those of Cuba.

5. *Florida.* The peninsula of Florida is America's Tropics. It stretches
300 miles from the boundary of Georgia where precautions are taken
to ward off the night frost, to the keys of its southern tip, where the
lemon, the lime and the mangrove flourish. Florida is a low limestone
platform, at no point more than about 100 feet above sea level. The
swamps, which make up about half the area of the state, generally
occupy depressions or sink holes in the limestone. In the northern and
central parts of the state a light sandy soil supports the fruit groves.
Numerous small lakes do something to reduce the danger of frost in the
groves that border them. To the south the cypress swamps take over
and continue, broken by lakes and by patches of land which rise a few
feet above the water, until they give place to the dreary waste of the
Everglades, a vast expanse of saw-grass rooting in shallow stagnant
water. Along the west the swamps run down to the coast, interrupted by
the few estuaries of the sluggish Floridan rivers. On the east a range of
dunes separates swamp from ocean, and on this narrow footing is concentrated the glamour of Miami (249,276), Fort Lauderdale and Palm
Beach.

— 10 —

The Great Plains

THE Great Plains constitute a distinct cultural region of the United States. It derives from more recent cultural origins than the South, and has a less distinctive character, but it too has made its own peculiar contribution to American life. Every child, dressed to look like a cowboy and sporting a brace of tin revolvers, is a living witness to the cultural impact of the Great Plains. In England, the "westerns" at the cinema and the cheap literature of the news-stand show that the traditions of the Plains, albeit trivial and superficial compared with the deeper cultural background of the South, have been disseminated over an incomparably larger area.

The Great Plains are difficult to define. They are, in the first place, a belt of level or rolling country which rises gently from the borders of the Mid-West and of the South and terminates at the steep rise of the Rocky Mountains. Secondly, it is a region of low rainfall, too low for the growth of trees except in damp hollows and along the watercourses. It is a grassland region, tall grass in the east, short in the west. The climate is one of extremes, with hot summers and winters bitterly cold in the north, and cool to the south.

THE PHYSICAL BACKGROUND. The Great Plains are built of level or only gently folded strata. In the north and east these are overlain by glacial drift. To the south these beds have been dissected enough to form a series of shallow valleys and low hills. In some parts the nearly level beds have given rise to escarpments which are continuous, in some instances, over enormous distances. On the borders of South Dakota and Wyoming the Black Hills break through the plains—an inlier of older rocks surrounded by a level sea of later and softer deposits. Amongst these are soft clays which have been gullied and eroded to form the Badlands of South Dakota, an area of great scenic attraction but little economic value.

These relief features are insufficient to detract from the predominant characteristic: "level plains, too wide for the eye to measure; green undulations, like motionless swells of the ocean; abundance of streams, followed through all their windings by lines of woods and scattered groves."[1]

Fig. 33. THE GREAT PLAINS AND THE WEST: RELIEF REGIONS

The rainfall of the Mid-West and South, more than adequate for crops, falls off abruptly along the eastern margin of the plains. Most of the plains area has less than 25 inches a year, and along the Rocky Mountain foothills this diminishes to less than 15. With the decline in the total amount of rainfall there goes a lessening degree of reliability. Out on the plains, crop cultivation becomes risky not because the average rainfall is too low, but because there is an even chance that in any

[1] Francis Parkman, *The Oregon Trail*, ch. IV.

one year the actual rainfall may fall very far short even of the average. The rainfall is strongly concentrated in the summer months, when storms occur of exceptional violence. These storms derive from the great heat of the continental interior and from the rapid convectional rise of air. They are sometimes accompanied by hail heavy enough to flatten crops and injure farm animals. More often there is thunder. "The thunder here is not like the tame thunder of the Atlantic coast. Bursting with terrific crash directly overhead", wrote Parkman, the nineteenth-century historian and traveller, "it roared over the boundless waste of prairie, seeming to roll around the whole circle of the firmament with a peculiar and awful reverberation. The lightning flashed all night, playing with its vivid glare upon the neighbouring trees, revealing the vast expanse of the plain, and then leaving us shut in as if by a palpable wall of darkness."[1]

This far from exhausts the climatic hazards of the Great Plains. All except its more northerly parts are liable to tornadoes in summer. On humid, sultry, summer days a heavy cloud bank may form; a vortex develops in the ascending air currents and a black, funnel-shaped cloud descends towards the earth. Where it touches the ground there is almost complete destruction of buildings and crops. These "twisters" sometimes cut a swathe of destruction for many miles across the plains.

The intense heat of summer contrasts with the bitter cold of winter. In the northern plains the January average is less than 15 degrees, and the blizzards lay down a snow-cover that may last for as much as three or even four months. Even in the southern plains, the cold arctic air sometimes pushes in, bringing zero temperatures even to Texas.

The natural vegetation of the Great Plains is grass. Towards the east this is tall grass with woodland and meadow along the valleys of the great rivers. Westwards the tall grass gives way to short, and in some parts this merges into an arid steppe. The whole of the Great Plains is grazing land, though the carrying power of the grassland is very small in areas where the rainfall is least.

The whole of the Great Plains is drained eastwards to the Mississippi. The Missouri, the greatest of the plains rivers, rises in the mountains of Montana. In its course, first to the east, then to the south-east, it gathers in succession the Yellowstone, Platte and Kansas Rivers. Each has numerous tributaries, some rising within the Rocky Mountain system, others taking their rise from springs within the Great Plains. Further to the south, the Arkansas and Red Rivers each collect a sheaf of tributaries from the plains before joining the Mississippi.

[1] Parkman, *op. cit.*, ch. V.

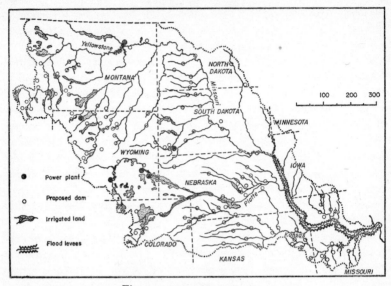

Fig. 34. THE MISSOURI BASIN
Showing the proposed reclamation projects.

The rivers of the Plains are, like the climate, boisterous and unruly,
now so shallow that a mile-wide river can be crossed on foot, now a
raging torrent, impossible to navigate and threatening destruction to
all who live near its banks. Francis Parkman thus described the Missouri, along whose banks he travelled in 1846 westwards from St.
Louis to Kansas City: "The broad and turbid river, with its eddies, its
sandbars, its ragged islands and forest-covered shores. The Missouri is
constantly changing its course; wearing away its banks on one side,
while it forms new ones on the other. Its channel is continually shifting.
Islands are formed, and then washed away, and while the old forests on
one side are undermined and swept off, a young growth springs up
from the new soil upon the other. With all these changes, the water is so
charged with mud and sand that, in spring, it is perfectly opaque."
When he returned in the autumn, the river "was fallen very low, and all
the secrets of its treacherous shallows were exposed to view. It was
frightful to see the dead and broken trees, thick-set as a military abattis,
firmly embedded in the sand, and all pointing downstream, ready to
impale any unhappy steamboat that at high water should pass over
them".[1]

---

[1] F, Parkman, *op. cit.*, ch. I.

HUMAN OCCUPANCE OF THE GREAT PLAINS. It was late before white men intruded into this region. Lack of fuel and shelter, the climatic hazards and the Indian tribes who, equipped with the horse, lived by hunting the bison, all combined to repel him. From the 1840's parties of settlers, trappers and prospectors crossed the plains, their covered waggons grouped into large convoys for greater protection, to the mountainous areas further west. The first permanent settlement was in the south where the hazards of the plains were least formidable. In the 1820's and 1830's settlements were made in what is to-day southern Texas, close to Rio Grande, and defended against Indians and Mexicans with the newly invented Colt revolver, without which the white occupation of the plains might have been very long delayed.

The plains were an obstacle to the westward expansion of the agricultural South. Too dry for cotton and corn, offering no remunerative employment for slaves, they were given over to a new economy, that of the range. The "cattle kingdom" began its colourful, uproarious rule about 1830. Spanish cattle from Mexico, with a few from the east, were introduced on the plains of Texas. They multiplied, and the problem of marketing them, before railways had reached the plains and when refrigeration was unknown, was serious. It was solved by the cattle trail. Thousands of half-wild cattle were driven north through the tall grass prairie until they reached the railhead in Kansas. The hazards of the journey, drought and stampedes, Indian attacks and white men's robberies are part of the lore of the west. In the sixties and seventies Abilene, Ka., became the foremost of the railhead cow-towns. "On the surface Abilene was corruption personified. Life was hectic, raw, lurid, awful. But the dance-hall, the saloon and the red light, the dissonance of immoral revelry punctuated by pistol shots, were but the superficialities which hid from view the deeper forces that were working themselves out round the new town. If Abilene excelled all later cow-towns in wickedness it also excelled them in service,—the service of bartering the beef of the South (i.e. south-west) for the money of the North."[1]

The range cattle industry itself was extended northwards, through Kansas and Nebraska to the high plains of Montana and Wyoming. Southern herds made the long journey as pressure of cattle on the southern ranges increased:

> It's whooping and punching and go on, little dogies,
> For you know Wyoming will be your new home.

.   .   .   .

[1] W. P. Webb, *The Great Plains* (Boston, 1931), p. 223.

Your mother she was raised waydown in Texas,
Where the Jimson weed and sand burs grow;
Now we'll fill you up on prickly pear and cholla
Till you are ready for the trail to Idaho.[1]

At first the half-wild cattle grazed promiscuously over the prairie, one herd distinguished from another only by the brand marks, and all of them rounded up annually to be sorted, marked or marketed. A more intensive, more scientific industry spread gradually, aided by the introduction of the steel windmill, which pumped water up from deep wells for the animals, and barbed wire, by means of which they could be kept from straying. The ranch replaced the range. Cattle were bred more scientifically and cared for more attentively than could ever have been possible on the range. The moister and better grasslands were thus enclosed. Meanwhile the unfenced, unwatered open range continued to support cattle, as it does to-day, on the thin dry grass of the western Great Plains.

In the meanwhile crop husbandry, spreading through the Mid-West, had reached the Great Plains. Along the eastern margin of the plains rainfall was enough and the black, chernozem soil more than adequate for wheat growing. Wheat farms spread into the Red River Valley of the Dakotas, and into Kansas and Nebraska. A growing demand for wheat, not only in the eastern states but also in Europe, raised the price and encouraged the wheat farmer ever deeper into the Great Plains. The climax was reached during the boom years of this century. Cultivation had been pushed into areas where the climate was quite unsuited to regular cropping. Land was cheap relative to the price of wheat, and the farmer was encouraged to use dry-farming methods. He took a crop every other year, allowing the land to lie fallow in the meanwhile. He harrowed the surface to produce a fine tilth. This checked evaporation and allowed moisture to accumulate. It also allowed the fierce winds of the prairies to strip the land of its dry, powdery topsoil.

The collapse in agricultural prices in 1930 brought disaster to the Great Plains. Farmers, unable either to hold their soil or sell their crop, abandoned their homesteads and trekked, west to California or east into moister lands where economic depression was not accompanied by the desolation of agricultural land. The saga of these years has been written by John Steinbeck in *The Grapes of Wrath*.

After the destruction of the soil, and the break-up of the precarious farming community of the drier plains, have come the attempts at prevention and restoration. The problems seemed more remote to most

[1] J. A. Lomax, *Cowboy Songs* (New York, 1948).

AND COULEE DAM, WASHINGTON. *Water is pumped from the lake formed by the main dam*
nto the old course of the Snake River, seen in the distance, where it is used for irrigation.

(I) AN OIL WELL IN THE DRY SAGE BRUSH COUNTRY OF WESTERN TEXAS. *In the dis is a butte, typical of the landscape of this country.*

(II) THE ARBUCKLE MOUNTAINS OF OKLAHOMA. *These are typical of the many moun areas which interrupt the Great Plains.*

Americans than that of the Tennessee Valley, and not until 1942 were steps taken towards a solution. Even so, the programme is limited to the drainage basin of the Missouri River.

The first problem is to check the run-off and limit the floods on this, the most unruly of American rivers. This is being done by means of a very large number of dams which will serve to hold back flood waters until the opportune moment for their release. The effect will be to smooth out the peak of the floods lower down the river. The dams will also provide the conditions for the generation of hydro-electric power and for irrigation along considerable tracts of the valleys. At the same time, levées are being extended, heightened or improved along much of the Missouri River. Contour ploughing or terracing on the hilly lands, and cropping in strips set across the prevailing wind direction on the flat lands, are being adopted to check erosion. The dry lands are being left under a permanent vegetation cover, and cropping limited to those where erosion is not serious.

AGRICULTURE IN THE GREAT PLAINS. The present agricultural pattern shows a wiser adjustment to the natural resources than that of a generation ago. The Great Plains may be divided into an eastern area where crop farming is the usual agricultural development, and a western, in which the livestock industry predominates, except in irrigated tracts along the valleys. The agricultural region of the plains is itself divisible into four distinct crop belts.

1. Most of North Dakota, with neighbouring areas of South Dakota, Montana and Minnesota, is marked out as an area of spring-sown wheat. The rainfall varies from 25 inches in the east to less than 15 in the west. The length of the growing period is from 100 to 120 days. In the Red River Valley to the east, on the silts left when the glacial Lake Agassiz dried up, mixed farming is practised. To the west there is an increasing specialization in wheat production, until the hazards of drought, and the difficulties of cultivating a terrain becoming steadily rougher, lead to the gradual replacement of crops by sheep and cattle. Along the western border of the spring wheat belt are large ranches which combine the rearing of beef cattle with the production of wheat and other spring-sown grains to be used as fodder.

In Montana, at the foot of the Rockies, where increasing proximity to the Pacific Ocean modifies the climate in some measure, are several outliers of the spring wheat belt.

2. South of the spring wheat belt, and covering parts of South Dakota and Nebraska, is the most westerly extension of the corn belt.

K

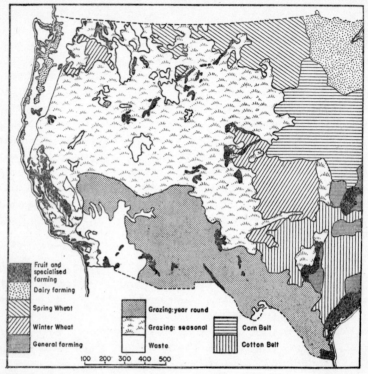

Fig. 35. THE GREAT PLAINS AND THE WEST: AGRICULTURAL REGIONS

But here the lower and less certain rainfall greatly limits the area under corn. Corn yields are unreliable; for this reason smaller quantities of stock are kept for fattening, and wheat gradually takes over.

3. Winter wheat is the dominant crop of Kansas and parts of Oklahoma, Texas, Colorado and Nebraska. Corn, sorghum, barley and other small grains are grown but hard winter wheat is the mainstay of farming. The grain is sown before the autumn frosts, and during late winter and spring there is a thin cover of growing wheat to reduce the risk of wind erosion. But the lack of a leguminous crop suited to the dry climate prevents the adoption of a sound crop rotation. This very often necessitates fallowing in alternate years, with a consequent increase of the erosion hazard.

4. Cotton has made its appearance on the Great Plains of Oklahoma and northern Texas in recent years. It is here very close to its climatic margin. The rainfall is but little more than 20 inches a year and is

liable to wide fluctuations. But cotton can stand some degree of drought, and such losses as there may be on this score appear to be offset by the absence of the boll weevil, which thrives only in a humid climate. On the northern margin of this area, the cotton is grown along with winter wheat and corn. Here the decision to grow wheat or cotton appears to be based upon the current prices of the two.

Between these crop areas and the Rocky Mountains is the range livestock region, an area where conditions of climate, relief and soil make animal husbandry more profitable than crop. The crop lands pass gradually into the range and the margin fluctuates with the expected income from animals and grain. There are also enclaves of range land lying back within the cropped areas, where the rougher terrain makes cultivation difficult or inadvisable: the Black Hills, the Badlands of South Dakota, the Nebraska Sand Hills and such scarpland areas as the Flint Hills of Kansas.

In the south of the range area winters are mild enough for animals to graze throughout the year. Some supplementary feeding may be necessary. Very little fodder crop is, or can be, grown except in the irrigated tracts along the rivers, and feed, much of it cotton seed cake, is brought into the area. Over most of the region the grazing is seasonal owing to the deep snow, the frozen subsoil and the complete interruption of plant growth. A large supply of fodder and hay is needed for winter consumption, much of it coming from the local areas of irrigated land. In this way the cattle industry depends upon the extension of flood control measures on the rivers.

Cattle are the most important occupants of the range lands. The carrying capacity of the pasture is generally small, and some ranches are as much as 100,000 acres in extent. Water is supplied from the perennial rivers or from wells. Winter shelter and feed are supplied, but beyond this the cattle require and receive but little care. They are rounded up once or twice a year, and selected animals sent east into the corn belt to be fattened (see p. 133).

Sheep are commonly reared where the land is too dry for cattle, and on the dry rough land of western Texas goats are kept. There are great risks in ranching. Droughts cause enormous losses in some years; winter blizzards may cut the animals off from their fodder and, hardy as they are, they cannot endure prolonged sub-zero weather.

The irrigated areas within the western plains are increasing in area and importance. Their role in supplying fodder to the range lands has already been noted. They are now producing large quantities of sugar beet, especially in Colorado, as well as irrigated vegetables of many kinds.

MINERAL RESOURCES. One would not expect a region such as this, composed almost wholly of unfolded strata of no great geological age, to be rich in minerals. The wealth of the area consists in, first, its coal seams and oil deposits, and, secondly, metalliferous ores associated with the "islands" of older and harder rock which occasionally rise above the level of the plains.

The geological conditions of the Great Plains are particularly suited to the formation of deposits of mineral oil and natural gas. The porous beds, slightly flexed, permit the pools of oil to form from the decaying organic matter contained in the rock. Commercial production of oil in Texas began in the 1890's and expanded very rapidly. The early production was from the coastal field, but after about 1910 the mid-continent field, stretching from Texas across Oklahoma into Kansas began to be developed. Then, about twenty years ago, the East Texas field, most productive of them all, was opened on the borders of Texas, Louisiana and Arkansas. At present the States of Texas, Louisiana and Oklahoma have about 67 per cent of the known oil reserves. At the present rate of consumption this supply may be expected to last for about ten years, but one may certainly attribute a longer life than this to the fields. Oil technology may be expected to improve, leading to a larger extraction from known fields. Further, new fields may be discovered and little known fields developed.

Oil is known to occur in small quantities along the foot of the Rocky Mountains in Colorado, Wyoming and Montana, though production from these fields is to-day quite small. Much of the petroleum is refined in close proximity to the fields but some is conveyed through a widespread net of oil pipes to refineries on the Gulf coast and in the north-eastern states. There are very large refineries close to the great consuming centres: at Whiting, near Chicago, and in the east.

A secondary product of the oil industry is natural gas. This is piped off and similarly distributed to the larger centres of population. Natural gas is a cheap as well as convenient domestic fuel, and in many parts of the north-eastern states is the commonest household fuel.

The coal deposits of the Great Plains are enormous in quantity but generally poor in quality. Bituminous coal is mined in small quantities in Montana, Wyoming, Colorado and New Mexico. In Montana, North Dakota and Wyoming are vast deposits of lignite and sub-bituminous coal. As a general rule this lies in level seams, of immense thickness, close to the surface. This region is remote from large markets for coal, and the huge potential output is very far from being realized.

The mining of metallic minerals is in effect limited to the Black Hills of South Dakota and to the north-western Ozarks (see p. 125). The Black Hills were the scene of a "gold rush" in the 1870's. They have continued to produce gold in small quantities, as well as silver, lead and zinc.

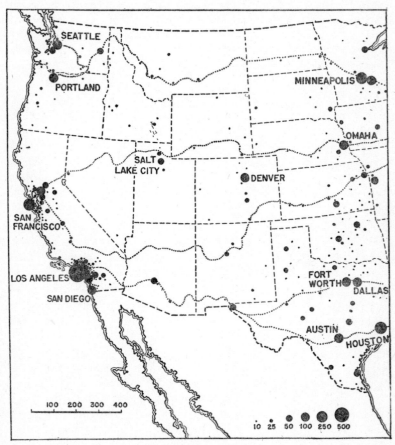

Fig. 36. THE GREAT PLAINS: CITIES AND TRANSPORT

THE CITIES OF THE GREAT PLAINS. The population of the Great Plains is predominantly rural. The farm is the chief means of livelihood; the city is the market centre for its surrounding farmland. A consequence of this is that cities are small and widely spaced. Denver, Colo.

(415,786), combines the functions of a mining and agricultural centre, and has further become a resort and the most important financial and business city of the Great Plains and Rocky Mountain region. Tulsa (182,740), and Oklahoma City, Okla. (243,504), owe their size largely to their recently acquired importance in the petroleum industry.

The communications, both by rail and road, lie mainly in an east-to-west direction. Towards the east they converge towards Chicago or St. Louis. To the west they diverge to cross the passes of the Rocky Mountains.

— II —

The West

WHEN the Okey family in *The Grapes of Wrath* left their home
on the blown soils of Oklahoma, they took the road westwards to what seemed to them the promised land of California. Their journey of 1,500 miles lay across the ranges and plateaux
of the American West. They crossed the Colorado River, the Mohave
Desert and at last topped Tehachapi Pass and looked down into the
great valley of California. Behind them were "the dry rocky country
. . . jagged broken peaks. . . . The little starved bushes, sage and greasewood. . . . The burnt land and the black cindery hills . . . terrible in the
reddening light of the setting sun." In front lay "the great valley below
them. . . . The vineyards, the orchards, the great flat valley, green and
beautiful, the trees set in rows, and the farm houses. . . . The grain
fields golden in the morning, and the willow lines, the eucalyptus trees
in rows. . . . The peach trees and the walnut groves, and the dark green
patches of orange. And red roofs among the trees, and barns—rich
barns. . . . The distance was thinned with haze, and the land grew
softer and softer in the distance." And the man from the parched
prairie of Oklahoma could only mutter: "I never knowed they was
anything like her."

The country through which they passed epitomizes the contrasts in
the West: the rich irrigated land set in the midst of the burning deserts;
the uninhabitable mountain ranges, and that Eden to which they were
making their way, the balmy Pacific coast itself. The West was opened
up to white settlement relatively late. A century ago there were only a
few thousand settlers in this vast region. The physical barriers that delayed the opening up of the region still present an obstacle—insuperable
in many parts—to human settlements.

THE LANDFORMS OF THE WEST.[1] For most of their length the Great Plains end abruptly on the west, and the Rocky Mountains rise suddenly and steeply. Sometimes outliers of the range, like the Bighorn Mountains of Wyoming, and the Big and Little Belt Mountains of Montana, lie out in front as if guarding the approaches to the greater fastnesses behind them. The main range has a remarkable continuity. From far to the north in Canada, through the Lewis Range of Montana; the Absaroka, Wind River and Medicine Bow ranges of Wyoming, the Front Range of Colorado, and the Sangre de Cristo and Sacramento Mountains of New Mexico, it continues for over 1,500 miles, broken only by the narrow, gorge-like valleys by which the rivers enter the Great Plains. West of these ranges crowd more, one behind the other, presenting a veritable defence in depth against penetration from the east: the tangled ranges of western Montana and northern Idaho, the splendours of the Yellowstone Park and the saw-like crest of the Teton Range; the Wasatch Mountains, rising precipitously from the Great Salt Lake, the Uinta Range, and the high plateau of western Colorado, with the snow-capped ranges rising from it.

The few breaks in these ranges are used by railway and road. In the north, the headwaters of the Missouri and of the west-flowing Snake and its tributaries have cut back to make a number of gaps through the mountains of north-western Montana. In south-western Wyoming the ranges become somewhat lower; here the Wyoming Basin gives access to the plateaux of Utah and Nevada without the need to cross any very high ranges. South Pass, leading into the basin, was discovered in about 1824 and, though replaced by a rather more southerly route now followed by the Union Pacific Railroad, was used by most of the early travellers and settlers, and was of inestimable value in the opening up of the west.

South of the Wyoming Basin, the great ranges of Colorado presented an almost insuperable barrier to the early travellers. It took the discovery of gold to bring people to these wastes, and even to-day there are few routes across the mountains between the Wyoming Basin and the plains of New Mexico. In the northern part of this state the Sangre de Cristo Mountains become lower and are more easily crossed. The southerly route to the West (see p. 16), the Santa Fé trail, made use of this to get around the obstacle of the mountains. The route is now followed by the Santa Fé Railroad.

The Rocky Mountain system is built of strongly folded strata, intruded locally by crystalline rocks. Very strong relief forms have been

[1] For map of relief regions, see Fig. 33, p. 130.

developed in almost all parts, and the whole region has a great scenic attraction. Most ranges rise to heights of 11,000 or 12,000 feet. The highest mountains, which lie in Colorado, rise to over 14,000 feet.

West of the Rocky Mountains is a region of lower altitude and generally of milder relief. This plateau region is limited on the west by further high ranges, resembling in their height and complexity the Rocky Mountains themselves. The intermontane plains are divisible, on the basis of their geological structure and resulting land forms, into three distinct units.

In the north the Rocky Mountains and the more westerly Cascade Mountains draw close together. Between them have been formed, through the outpouring from many unseen volcanic fissures, the huge lava plains of the Snake River Plateau. The basaltic lava has accumulated in places to a depth of 5,000 feet. The region must originally have been a vast level plain, but the Columbia River and its great tributary, the Snake, and the many smaller streams have carved deep valleys across the region. The somewhat porous nature of the rock, and the considerable depth to which the rivers have been incised in the plateau, combine to make the whole region rather dry. Springs are common enough on the valley sides, but over the plateau surface, where there is sometimes a good soil, moisture is often too little for cultivation. The plains of the Snake River Valley support only a vegetation of dry grass and sage bush and are at best grazing land. In the Columbia Valley, however, the soils are good and agriculture, assisted by irrigation, is important. The Columbia River and its tributaries are already dammed in a number of places and the water stored up is used both to generate power and to irrigate the land below the dams. The most ambitious of these installations is the Grand Coulee dam, by which the water of the Columbia River is made to flow through an ancient glacial spillway to irrigate a large tract of fertile soil lower down the formerly dry valley.

The Columbia River has been described as "the greatest potential source of usable energy of any river on the North American continent."[1] Numerous other dams have either been built or are in prospect, and in its integration of power generation, irrigation and land reclamation, the Columbia system may in the very near future rival the Tennessee and the Missouri.

South of the lava flows of the Columbia and Snake River Plateau is the *Great Basin*. This is a vast plateau lying generally at an altitude of between 3,000 and 7,000 feet. It is highest towards the north, where

[1] G. B. Barbour, in *G.J.*, XCVI (1940), p. 233.

it rises from the Snake River Plateau. Its level drops southwards towards the Colorado River, and along the Mexican border is not much over 1,000 feet. To the west the Great Basin is limited by the high ranges of the Cascade Mountains and Sierra Nevada; to the east, by the Rocky Mountains and the high plateaux, to be described below, of Utah and Arizona. The dominant topographical feature of the Great Basin is the great number of short, straight ranges, with steep sides and sharp serrated crests, that lie roughly from north to south. These ranges are relatively short; few are as much as 100 miles in length, and the transcontinental routes have no difficulty in passing around their extremities. These mountains are the product of an extensive faulting of the whole region, and consist mostly of faulted and tilted blocks. Between the mountains the plateau is almost level. Over large areas there is a deep spread of alluvium either spread by rivers issuing from the mountains or laid down in shallow lakes that in glacial times covered considerable areas. Some relics of these once extensive lakes remain, occupying hollows in the plateau surface. The Great Salt Lake of Utah is the largest.

Tributaries of the Snake River have cut back into the Great Basin along the north, and towards the south it is crossed by the Colorado River, but between these two there is no river that makes its way to the sea, or, indeed, much surface drainage at all. Rainfall is low throughout the Great Basin, and is less than 10 inches a year over much of it. Most rivers flow only intermittently and end in shallow lakes or salty swamps where the water evaporates into the dry air. The Humboldt is the largest of such rivers. It flows westwards across the Basin to lose itself in the salty flats of the Carson Sink, at the foot of the Sierra Nevada.

East of the Great Basin are the plateaux of the Colorado Valley. The Green River, the major tributary of the Colorado, rises in the Wyoming Basin, trenches the Uinta Mountains and, after its junction with the Colorado River, flows in a deeply incised and highly spectacular valley across the Colorado Plateau. The plateau is built of level or nearly level strata. To the north-west these beds rise to the high plateau of Utah, famous for its highly coloured rocks and the strange beauty of Bryce Canyon and Zion National Park. Nearer the Colorado River the plateau is increasingly dissected; "no equally large plateau . . . has the ruggedness of these canyon lands". Soil erosion has become serious on the steep, denuded slopes, and the great river carries an immense burden of silt down towards the sea. Across the Arizona border there are fewer tributaries, and the river flows for some 200 miles through the Grand Canyon, one of the most spectacular landforms in the whole continent. Nothing gives a more vivid impression of the power of natural erosion than this chasm, in places 5,000 feet deep, at the bottom of which swirls the yellow river.

For most of its length the Colorado River lies too far below the plateau surface to have any value for irrigation. It is only a barrier to travel, with no crossing for some 200 miles, but in the last 300 miles of its course the valley widens and then expands into a broad, rolling area of desert. This is the Sonoran Desert, in reality a southward extension of the Great Basin, and, like it, distinguished by fault-bounded mountains and depressions. Deepest of these depressions is the Salton Sink, a large area west of the Colorado River, lying more than 200 feet below sea level. In its midst is the shallow, brackish Salton Sea. The whole is as strongly reminiscent of the Dead Sea, as the Colorado River is of the Nile. It was no great engineering problem to feed water from the Colorado River into the Imperial Valley, as the Salton Sink has been renamed. There are now two large canals, fed from behind dams on the main river, and the Imperial Valley is an important area for the production of irrigated cotton and fruit crops. But the Colorado is a very turbulent river, liable to violent floods, and sometimes too much water has flowed down into the Imperial Valley, destroying the farms and citrus groves. It was partly to regulate its flow, partly to secure more water for irrigation and even for the supply of distant Los Angeles, that the Hoover (Boulder) Dam was built.

South-east of the Colorado River the plateau is less broken. Over great areas it forms merely a yellow or red expanse of desert, broken only by the steep-sided and tabular mesas which are dotted about its surface. Its only vegetation is a thin, coarse, drought-resisting grass interspersed with yucca and cactus. This is the home of the most interesting of the surviving Indian peoples, the Hopi, Yuma and Navajo. They continue to live in villages—still called by the Spanish name of *Pueblos* —cultivating their corn patches and making quaint carvings for sale to the tourists. They are a colourful people, who have polished up their traditional dances and customs since they discovered that these are a source of considerable financial gain from the traveller.

West of the Great Basin is a chain of mountains which stretches from far inside Canada to the Mexican border, broken only by the gap cut by the Columbia River. The Pacific coast ranges are, in fact, a double range. The Cascade Mountains and Sierra Nevada border the Columbia Plateau and the Great Basin. West of this is a belt of lower land, forming in the north the Puget Sound lowlands and the Willamette Valley; in the south, the Great Valley of California. Separating these from the sea are the coast ranges of the United States. In the centre, between the head of the Willamette Valley and the northern end of the Great Valley, the Cascade Mountains and the coastal range are contiguous.

The Sierra Nevada is one of the highest and least interrupted ranges in the continent. It is a faulted block, and in its general shape resembles the lesser ranges of the Great Basin. The highly disturbed strata have been intruded by granite masses. The differential erosion of the two has produced complex landforms. One of the most beautiful sections of the range has been constituted the Yosemite National Park. The eastern margin of the Sierra Nevada, where it overlooks the Great Basin, is remarkably straight and abrupt, and has been developed along a fault line. Above this scarp is Mount Whitney (14,495 feet), the highest mountain in the United States. Only 60 miles away is Death Valley, 280 feet below sea level, resulting from the down-faulting of a block in the Great Basin. There is no easy crossing of the Sierra Nevada between Tehachapi Pass in southern California and Donner Pass, where the main transcontinental route crosses. North of the Donner Pass, the range becomes much lower and more broken by gaps and passes. Under the name of the Cascade Mountains it continues into Canada. The Cascade range has been the scene of volcanic activity in comparatively recent times. Mount Shasta (14,162 feet) and Lassen Peak (10,453 feet), both in northern California, are still active volcanoes. Mount Hood (11,245 feet) in Oregon and Mount Rainier (14,408 feet) in Washington are both extinct volcanoes of great natural beauty. In Oregon is the Crater Lake, the caldera of an immense, extinct volcano.

The coastal ranges are much lower and more interrupted even than the Cascades. They culminate in the north in Mount Olympus, which looks across the Juan de Fuca Strait to Canada. To the south, a series of short segments of mountain extends through Washington and Oregon. Between Astoria and Portland the Coast Range is crossed by the Columbia River. In south-west Oregon and northern California the Coast Range merges into the higher massif of the Klamath Mountains, which in turn passes into the Cascade Range. Stretching south from the Klamath Mountains is the coastal range of California. This is made up of parallel or sub-parallel ranges of no great height, lying diagonally to the coast. Where they reach the ocean they form headlands, which are separated from one another by deep bays and tracts of lowland. Most important of such inlets is that formed in central California by San Francisco Bay.

In the extreme south the coastal range curves to the east, culminates in the San Bernardino Mountains and then subsides into the Sonoran Desert.

Between the coastal range on the one hand and the Cascade-Sierra Nevada Range on the other lie the most populous and the most intensively developed areas of the whole American West. These are, in the north, the lowlands around Puget Sound, continued southwards in the Willamette Valley and, secondly, the Great Valley of California. Both are immense structural depressions, filled in with Tertiary, glacial and recent deposits. Each is almost completely surrounded by mountains which in some degree cut off the rainfall, and each has a soil greatly superior to that of surrounding regions.

Puget Sound is the

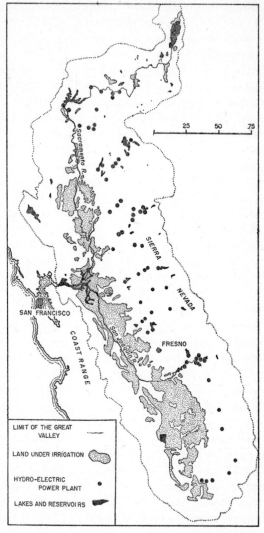

Fig. 37. THE GREAT VALLEY OF CALIFORNIA

most southerly extension of the fjord coast of British Columbia. It is an intricate system of waterways, slowly silting with the sediment brought down from the surrounding mountains. Around the Sound is a belt of flat alluvial land, from the margin of which the mountains —the Cascades on the east, the isolated massif of Mount Olympus on the west—rise abruptly. To the south the plain narrows, and only a very narrow strip of lowland links it with the valley of the Columbia River. The Columbia, like Puget Sound, has also been drowned by a recent rise of the sea level. From below Portland a widening estuary stretches westwards, across the line of the Coast Range, to the sea. At Portland, the Columbia is joined by the Willamette River, whose valley continues the Puget Sound lowlands towards the south.

The Klamath Mountains break the continuity of this Pacific coast depression or trough. But, south of Mount Shasta, it reappears and continues for over 400 miles between the Coast Range and the Sierra Nevada. This is the Great Valley of California, a tract of level land, with deep alluvial soil, over fifty miles in width. Its ring of mountains is broken only on the west, where a gap in the Coast Range gives access to the ocean. A great number of rivers descend from the Sierra Nevada, are gathered by the southward flowing Sacramento and the north-flowing San Joaquin, and their waters delivered, through the gap on the Coast Range, into San Francisco harbour.

CLIMATE, VEGETATION AND SOILS. There is great variety in the climate of the West owing, in part, to the great latitudinal expanse of the territory, in part to the mountains which, in a sense, make their own climate. If we exclude the areas of high mountain, in which conditions of extreme cold prevail for most of the year, there remain four distinct climatic and vegetation regions in the west.

By far the most extensive is the region of hot summers, cool or cold winters and low rainfall which covers the northern intermontane plains and the high plateaux of Utah, Colorado and New Mexico and the Rocky Mountains. Rainfall, except on the mountains, is less than 20 inches a year, and in many parts it is less than 10. Most of the higher ground is forested with coniferous trees. The lower has often only a sparse covering of drought-resisting shrubs, sage bush and greasewood. Agriculture is practised in this climatic belt without the help of irrigation. Dry farming has been important on the Snake River plains, but has led to serious erosion. In many parts the soils are naturally fertile, and, without irrigation, yield heavy crops. Along the valleys of the Snake, Columbia and their tributaries, at the foot of the Wasatch Range in Utah, and in many parts of the Colorado Plateau irrigation agriculture is practised.

Towards the south this region of steppe passes into the second climatic region, the desert. Here the rainfall is generally below 10 inches a year, and agriculture is impossible without irrigation. All seasons are hotter than in the steppe belt, and near the Mexican border cotton and citrus fruits can be grown by irrigation. The natural vegetation is coniferous forest on the mountains and, over the plateaux, a thin covering of xerophytic shrubs. The creosote bush and mesquite grass are the commonest plants, with, towering above them, the yucca and the bare, branching arms of the cactus.

Large parts of the intermontane region are devoid of soils. The bare rock, yellow, red or brown in most parts, yet more gaudily coloured in the Painted Desert of Arizona and Bryce Canyon, supports a sage-hued vegetation which roots in its joints and cracks. Along the valleys is alluvium, often waiting only for irrigation to become a flowering oasis. In the hollows of the Great Basin, where lakes have dried up or the rivers evaporate away, the soil is so impregnated with salts as to be useless for agriculture. Only in the extreme north, in the Palouse area of the Snake and Columbia Valleys, are there soils as rich and as extensive as the black soils of the Prairies. Here the severe winter and the low rainfall combine to produce chernozem soils. But the rainfall is often too low for regular cropping, dry farming is practised, and the danger of wind erosion is consequently high.

The Cascade Mountains are a climatic divide. To the east is semi-desert. The mountains themselves are wet and forested, and to the west are the rain-soaked hills of the coast range, with their mild winters and cool summers. The Pacific North-West, the strip of territory in Washington and Oregon lying between the Cascade Mountains and the sea, resembles north-west Europe. It has a cool, cloudy climate, with rain at all seasons. When white men reached this region they found a thick cover of continuous forest, coniferous on higher ground, mixed in the valleys. Forests remain over the mountains, vast stands of Douglas fir, red cedar and spruce, which make it one of the foremost sources of softwood timber in the United States.

The soils of the Pacific North-West, like those of north-western Europe, are leached and poor; most are classified as podsols. Along the Willamette Valley, in the rain shadow of the Coast Range, conditions are drier, and the soils are brown earth, approximating rather to those of the Palouse region beyond the Cascades.

Most of California, lastly, has a Mediterranean-type climate. Summers are hot and winters mild. Frosts occur, even in the Great Valley, but periods of continuous cold are met with only in the Sierra Nevada. Off the Californian coast there flows a cool ocean current resulting from the upwelling of water from the deep ocean. Warm air from the Pacific Ocean is chilled as it passes over this cool water body and fogs are formed. Sea fogs characterize much of the Californian coast, and the city of San Francisco owes its relatively low summer temperatures chiefly to its liability to fog which greatly reduces the insolation. As it is blown inland towards the Great Valley the fog very quickly disperses as the moisture is reabsorbed into the dry air.

Rainfall occurs chiefly in the winter months, and the summer, the chief growing season, is dry, thus heightening the need for irrigation. On the western flank of the Sierra Nevada the winter precipitation comes mainly as snow. Snowfalls are very heavy and prolonged. Attempts to keep the roads and railways open across the mountains are often defeated, and one not infrequently hears in winter of travellers snowbound as they cross the Donner Pass.

In the extreme south of California, even the winter rain becomes small in volume and unreliable. The city of Los Angeles lies in an almost desert setting, where the clear skies and long vistas encouraged the early film industry as it to-day assists the astronomical work at Mount Palomar.

The natural vegetation of such lands is adapted to a long period of summer drought. Where the winter rainfall is small, as in the Great Valley, the natural vegetation cover was drought-resisting bunch grass, but generally the cover was of xerophytic shrubs, known as *chaparral*. On the mountains, where the rainfall increases, this gives way to coniferous forest. Vast stands of pine cover the slopes of the Sierra Nevada and, in part, those of the Coast Range. The trees are often of enormous size, and in the Sierra are stands of the giant sequoia, the largest tree known.

HUMAN OCCUPANCE OF THE WEST. In the eighteenth and early nineteenth centuries the American West was thought of as being made up of the "Great American Desert". The name was enough to deter travellers and settlers. Only in the nineteenth century, when the reports of explorers became available, were the limits of this great desert reduced and its frightfulness abated. There were, nevertheless, obstacles enough in the mountains and canyons, the lack of water and the extremes of temperature, to deter the most intrepid adventurer. It needed, in the early nineteenth century, a very strong inducement to take settlers to the West.

When white men first came they found, in the south-west, Indian tribes, such as the Hopi and Navajo. They lived in villages, often sited high on edges of buttes; their houses were made of adobe, i.e. sundried mud bricks; they practised agriculture and used irrigation to grow their corn. Further north were Indians who practised a hunting

AN OX-BOW ON THE RIO GRANDE RIVER. *The main course of the river is seen in the ance. Beyond the river is Mexico. In the foreground is irrigated farmland.* LANDSCAPE IN THE DRY LANDS OF ARIZONA.

(I) THE TETON RANGE, FROM THE EAST. *The mountains lie on the border of Wyoming and Ida.*
(II) YOSEMITE NATIONAL PARK, CALIFORNIA. *The photograph shows the Half-dome wh.*
overlooks the valley. It is an igneous mass, part of which was cut away by a former valley glacie

and fishing economy. Into the area of the southern tribes came Spanish missionaries, followed by Spanish settlers and soldiers. The Spanish and then the Mexican influence was strong in the south-west. The present boundary with Mexico was not finally established until 1853. Before this a large part of California, Arizona, New Mexico and Texas had formed part of Mexico. The Spanish influence remains conspicuous. Many of the older place-names—Albuquerque, Santa Fé, Los Angeles, Tucson—are Spanish and the current pronunciation of them is often enough Spanish, too. Public buildings and even private houses often have a Spanish character. Church buildings in the south-west, with their baroque affinities, are utterly different from the classic simplicity of their counterparts in New England. The two sorts of architecture derive from opposite cultural traditions. The grape vine was brought into California by the Spaniards in the eighteenth century. In the cities near the Mexican border there remains to-day a considerable Spanish-speaking population, and always there is a seasonal movement of labourers from Mexico.

The opposite extremity of the region, the Pacific North-West, was also early in attracting settlers, though for quite different reasons. Its luxurious forests not only offered a wealth of timber, but harboured fur-bearing animals in such numbers that the region inevitably attracted the adventurous trapper and trader. Despite the establishment of a trading post on the Columbia River early in the century, settlers came very slowly. The journey through Wyoming and Idaho was arduous in the extreme, and there seemed no way of despatching heavy freight between the Missouri River and the Pacific coastlands.

Small groups of settlers had pressed across the Great Plains and into the Rocky Mountains. Again the hazards of the journey and the uncertainty of what lay at its end prevented all except a few eager, reckless individuals from taking the route. Amongst them were the Mormons, who, in the late forties, trekked through the Rocky Mountains and settled along the foot of the Wasatch Mountains. Their desire for complete freedom to practise their strange religion was amply satisfied in the Utah Basin. They were, as they wished to be, a separate and self-sufficing community. They developed irrigation and created an oasis in the barren Utah plateau.

But it was not until gold was discovered that settlers came in large numbers. It took the expectation of easy fortunes to draw farmers and clerks, sailors and factory hands away from the populous east into the empty lands of the West. Gold was discovered in the Sacramento Valley in 1848. It was probably not the earliest discovery, but it gave prospect

L

of riches, it received great publicity, and the stream of migrants set out, full of hope, for the gold fields. In 1849 the flood of prospectors reached California. New workings were opened further south in the San Joaquin Valley. The easily worked alluvial deposits were quickly exhausted. Some of the miners returned to the East; some moved on to othermine-fields; some stayed as permanent settlers, breaking in the agricultural land in the Great Valley and building up its irrigation system.

In the meanwhile gold was discovered in other parts of the West. It was found in the Rocky Mountains of British Columbia. Then, ten years after the Californian discovery, it was found on the other side of the Sierra Nevada. This was the beginning of the Nevada rush. Mine towns sprang up, many of them short-lived, all of them rowdy, colourful, lawless. The Nevada mining towns had a longer run than most. The Comstock Lode, discovered in the opening stages of the rush, developed into a highly important source of silver. The Nevada boom attracted so many settlers that the territory gained statehood in a very short time, but, unlike California, Nevada had no resources to employ the miners as the ores gave out. The population, after its sudden rise, has declined steadily and Nevada is now the least populous state in the Union.

From Nevada the centre of mining interest moved to the Rocky Mountains of Colorado; then to Idaho and Montana. Few mining towns showed any degree of permanence. At best they were towns of wooden shacks and saloons, separated by dirt roads, quickly built and readily abandoned. The West is littered with the remains of "ghost towns", rotting into the ground as plants and trees take over. They represent one—perhaps the most romantic—of the sequential stages in the human occupance of the West. At the very least, the search for gold brought in settlers and led to a very much more thorough exploration of the country than might otherwise have taken place.

By 1890 the main railways to the Pacific had been completed. They offered to many areas capable of an agricultural development an opportunity to market their farm products in the cities of the East or in those of the Pacific coast. The grasslands of the Columbia and Snake River valleys were occupied in the 1870's and 1880's; the farms and orchards of the Willamette Valley and Puget Sound were laid out; vineyards and orchards were beginning to spread over the hills of southern California.

The last phase in the human occupance of the West was made possible by the large-scale development of irrigation along the great rivers, particularly the Columbia and Snake, the Sacramento and San Joaquin and the Colorado.

THE PATTERN OF AGRICULTURE. The agricultural pattern of the West is more complex than that of any other part of the United States. This is because of the great variations in climate, the range of altitude, and the introduction of a highly specialized agriculture on irrigated lands. Some areas (see fig. 35) are unfit for agriculture however rudimentary: the Cascade and Coast Ranges and much of the desert South-West. Most of the remainder is fit only for grazing. In the southern part of the Great Basin the winters are mild enough for the animals to remain out and find enough feed through the winter. Little fodder can be produced in the dry climate, and supplementary feed is brought in from the Cotton Belt or from the irrigated valleys. Cattle, sheep and, in western Texas, goats are grazed. "Feeder" cattle and sheep are shipped out of the grazing areas into the irrigated lands, with their mixed farming, or the Middle West.

Further north, the grazing is seasonal owing to the severity of the winter, and the rough grazing of summer has to be supplemented by a heavy consumption of fodder. It is more necessary here that the ranches should have access to a regular supply of hay and fodder. Some ranches are able to produce their own from irrigated bottom-lands. Others rely on the small but intensively cultivated areas along the valleys. On the mountain slopes the open season for grazing is even shorter than on the plateaux owing to the prolonged snow-cover. It often happens that stock spends the summer months on the highest land, grazes the slopes for a period in spring and autumn and is given fodder and hay in the more sheltered parts of the plateau during the winter.

Crop farming occupies only a small proportion of the area of the intermontane plateaux, but in the extreme north, between the Cascade Mountains and the mountains of Idaho, is an area of grain cultivation. Winter wheat is grown though the area is climatically somewhat marginal, and the autumn-sown crop is occasionally killed by the winter frost. If this happens, a spring wheat is seeded in April. Winter wheat is preferred because it helps to hold the soil during the winter months when the blowing of the topsoil sometimes attains dangerous proportions. A problem has been to find a crop, suited to the dry climate, which can be grown in rotation with wheat. In the drier western part of the area, a wheat crop is commonly taken in alternate years, and the land is left fallow in the intervening years. To the east, field peas, barley and oats are sometimes grown in rotation with wheat, which nevertheless remains the dominant crop.

Dairy farming is the chief agricultural pursuit in the lowlands of Puget Sound and the Willamette Valley, but is combined with the growing of vegetables and fruit. The region with its mild temperatures and considerable rainfall is well suited to the cultivation of meadow grass and fodder crops. Small areas of intensive dairy farming line the Pacific coast and extend southwards into California. They are chiefly important for the production of liquid milk for the urban markets.

The least extensive and most valuable of the agricultural lands of the West are those in which a very intensive and highly specialized cultivation, frequently dependent on irrigation, is practised. It includes the irrigated cotton-fields of the Gila and Rio Grande Valleys and of the southern part of the Great Valley of California; the citrus fruit, grapes and rice of the Great Valley; temperate fruit in Washington and Oregon; sugar beet in Wyoming and Montana; and potatoes in Idaho.

In the forested mountains of the Pacific North-West the lumbering industry is the most important. The vast stands of huge Douglas fir make this one of the richest reserves of timber in the continent. Lumber from the mills of Washington and Oregon is mostly exported by sea to other parts of the United States and to foreign countries. Other areas of marketable lumber are less accessible than the Pacific North-West, but smaller quantities of softwood lumber are cut in Idaho and Montana and in the Rocky Mountains of Wyoming, Colorado and New Mexico. In the South-West the little lumber that grows on the mountains is not usually of a marketable quality.

MINERALS AND MINING. It was, as we have seen, the mineral wealth of the West that attracted the larger number of its early settlers. The West is relatively deficient in coal but is rich in petroleum and the non-ferrous metals. Petroleum is important only in southern California —in the Los Angeles hinterland and in the most southerly extension of the Great Valley. Reserves have been proved further north in the Great Valley, and their development is now taking place. The most spectacular development of oil drilling has taken place around Los Angeles, where a forest of masts has arisen each tapping a minute area of oil-field, some no bigger than a domestic building plot. This extraordinary situation has resulted from the working of oil in a densely populated area with a fragmented land ownership and high land values.

Gold and silver mining remain in the western states though of diminished importance. California retains its position as the leading gold-producing state. The metal comes from the western flanks of the Sierra Nevada, from the area where the alluvial gold was worked a century ago, but mining is now carried on in the rock by means of shafts and galleries. Gold is also obtained from mines in Arizona, Colorado and the more northerly Rocky Mountain states.

Nevada, long famous for the silver from its Comstock Lode, has yielded place to Idaho, Montana and Utah as a silver producer. In those "silver states", the heavy silver dollar piece remains in common currency, as a concession to local interest and pride, whereas elsewhere this coin has been replaced by the more convenient if less sanitary "dollar bill".

Most important of the non-ferrous minerals in the West is copper. The ore mined is commonly of a low grade. It is stripped and pulverized by means of huge machines; the ore is separated from the gangue, or waste, by flotation and then sent to the smelter. Huge deposits of low-grade copper ore are worked at Bingham Canyon, Utah, and at Morenci, Bisbee, Ajo and Globe in Arizona. Lead and zinc are also mined. The Coeur d'Alene district of northern Idaho is outstanding for both; the Butte district of Montana for zinc, and both are obtained in the mineralized areas of Utah, Arizona, New Mexico and Colorado. Many other minerals, amongst them antimony, magnesium, manganese, mercury, molybdenum, tungsten and vanadium, are obtained in important quantities from the West, and the production of many of these is more than adequate to meet United States demand.

POPULATION AND SETTLEMENT. The West has to-day a population of about 19,500,000. The greater part of this is rural and engaged in some agricultural pursuit. Cities are few and small except along the coast of the Pacific Ocean and, except in the latter area, their function is rather narrowly specialized. They are mining centres, such as Cœur d'Alene, Bingham and Bisbee; or market centres for an area of specialized agricultural production, such as Ogden, Utah (57,112) or Boise, Idaho (34,393). Some are route centres at the convergence of railways and roads across the mountains: Spokane, Wash. (161,721) and Phoenix, Ariz. (106,818); yet others are resorts, where tourists may enjoy the warmth in winter or the coolness in summer, and from which they can with a minimum of effort visit the natural wonders of the region. Some, like Reno, Nev. (32,497), owe their significance to the eccentricities of the state laws, which permit of gambling or easy divorce.

Amongst the many small cities are the few large, where prosperity is more broadly based on manufacturing and commerce. In the intermontane basin only two such cities deserve mention: Salt Lake City, Utah, and Spokane, Wash.

Salt Lake City (182,121) is the largest between the Rocky Mountains and the Pacific coast. It is well placed on the east-to-west routes, it is the centre of well-farmed irrigated land and, above all, it is the headquarters of Mormon faith. It owes much of its prosperity, as well as the beauty of its planning and its wide tree-lined streets, to the energy and foresight of these "latter-day saints", who could show themselves to be worldly enough when necessary.

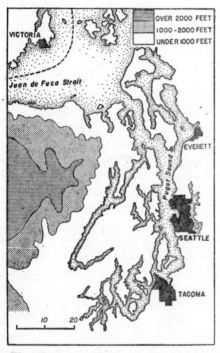

Fig. 38. PUGET SOUND AND THE SITE OF SEATTLE

Spokane (161,721), in addition to its significance on the more northerly Rocky Mountain routes—two of the transcontinental railways run through the city—is the milling and business centre for the Columbia Valley wheat belt.

The Cities of the Pacific coast can be grouped into those in the far north-west and those in central and southern California. The branching waterways of Puget Sound provide many admirable harbours, which were used early in the nineteenth century for the shipment of timber. Tacoma, Wash. (143,673), became the leading port in the nineteenth century, carrying on trade with Alaska and the Orient. As a port and commercial centre it has now been outdistanced by Seattle, but it remains an important industrial city, with very large sawmills and pulp, paper and furniture works.

Seattle, Wash. (467,591), lies lower down the waters of the Sound, and thus is more accessible to sea-going ships. Both port and city grew rapidly with the opening up of Alaska. Landward communications with the East are better than for almost any other Pacific coast city. In addition to its foreign trade, Seattle has important industries concerned with the fabricating of wood and pulp products, the preserving of fruit and other products of the agricultural hinterland, and the building and repair of ships.

Portland, Or. (406,406), lies on the Columbia River, over 100 miles from its mouth. Though the river is here easily navigable, Portland cannot compete in commercial significance with its neighbour, Seattle. It is rather the capital of the rich farmlands of the Cowlitz and Willamette Valleys. It is also an industrial city, with timber industries and a woollen textile industry based on the local resources in hydroelectric power and the wool from the grazing lands of the Great Basin.

Numerous smaller towns lie around the shores of Puget Sound and along the Pacific coast. Many are fishing ports; the fishing industry is an important one. The salmon, by far the most important fish, is caught, usually in nets, as it enters the rivers to whose headstreams it comes to spawn. The chief difficulty in the way of the continued prosperity of the salmon fisheries lies in the numerous works on the rivers which, in one way or another, prevent the salmon from ascending the streams to lay their eggs. All newly constructed dams in this region are equipped with "fish-ladders" up which it is hoped that the salmon will learn to swim or jump. In recent years the preparation and canning of tuna fish has attained a considerable importance in the fishing communities along the Californian coast. Other fish are landed, especially halibut, herring and pilchard.

Between northern Oregon and central California are few cities, all of them very small. The country is mountainous and communications difficult. The Great Valley of California, however, provides the natural conditions in which cities may develop: rich agricultural land, intensively developed, mineral resources, a coastal location with good harbours, and convenient landward connections with the interior of the United States. In the Great Valley are cities of medium size where the oranges, grapefruit and cotton are collected and despatched. Some have attracted manufacturing industries whose markets are likely to lie in this farming country. Largest of these inland cities is Sacramento (137,572). Stockton (70,853), Fresno (91,669) and Bakersfield (34,784) are others (see fig. 36).

San Francisco. The Sacramento and San Joaquin Rivers unite to discharge into a large bay of complex shape which communicates with the ocean through the narrow gap in the Coast Range known as the Golden Gate. Inside the headlands is one of the finest natural harbours

in the world. The Spaniards established the mission station of San
Francisco on its shore in the eighteenth century, but for a century the
settlement remained small and the port unimportant. Then, in succession, the gold rush, the development of agriculture in the Great Valley,
the completion of the transcontinental railways and the opening up of
trade across the Pacific Ocean to the Orient added to the importance
of the site. The metropolitan area of San Francisco has to-day a
population of almost a million and a half.

Fig. 39. THE SITE OF SAN FRANCISCO

The branching waterways of the harbour add to its beauty,
but detract from the conven-ience of movement. The railroads
made their termini on the eastern shore of the harbour at Oakland,
and ferry-boats carried passen-gers and freight across to San
Francisco. In 1936 the Oakland-San Francisco bridge was completed. In the next year another and similar great bridge was
built across the Golden Gate.
The growth of Berkeley, Oakland
and Alameda on the eastern shore of the bay was due in the first place
to the convenience of transport inland. They received a considerable
impetus when the city of San Francisco was largely destroyed in 1906
by an earthquake and by the fire that followed. San Francisco is to-day
the chief port; Oakland and Alameda are the industrial centres and
Berkeley the seat of the University of California, one of the largest in
the world.

Los Angeles. It is easy to explain the growth of San Francisco; Los
Angeles defies any facile explanation. It is very largely a development
of the present century. It lies in the midst of an arid plain, bounded on
the north and east by the San Gabriel and San Bernardino Mountains.
The cultivation of citrus fruit and the manufacture of moving pictures,
for both of which the climate was excellent, attracted a considerable
population. The discovery of oil brought about a commercial "boom".
Other industries moved in, often enough for no other reason than that
the climate was good and there was already present a labour supply

and a market. The aircraft industry, steel-making and shipbuilding are the latest additions, in part or as a result of government policy during the war years. It seems ironic that a region which only a generation ago was attracting people by the excellence of its climate and the beauty of its scenery, should now repel them with the thickness of its industrial "smog".

The metropolitan area of Los Angeles is a vast sprawling area—one of the largest built-up areas in the world. Los Angeles (1,970,358) itself is the largest unit in this complex; around it is a circle of others: Santa Monica (71,595), Hollywood, Glendale (95,702), Pasadena (104,577), Alhambra (51,359), Long Beach (250,767) and many others. On the whole they are well laid out, with wide streets and thoroughfares for fast traffic, so necessary in as vast an urban area as this. Los Angeles has few of the blemishes which we commonly associate with a city that has grown too fast. A little over a hundred miles to the south is San Diego (334,387), a city of even more recent and more rapid growth, with naval dockyards and aircraft factories. Fundamentally this rapid growth of cities and industries along the Pacific coast from Seattle to San Diego reflects the recent interest, commercial as well as strategic, which the United States has acquired in the Pacific Ocean and the Orient.

— 12 —

Canada: East

MOST of eastern Canada is occupied by a shield-like mass of ancient and resistant rocks. These are metamorphosed and in parts highly mineralized. Through a series of cycles of erosion and rejuvenation the whole region has been reduced to a rolling plateau. Its greatest heights, which lie to the east, are less than 4,000 feet above sea level. Their bare rounded summits, worn smooth by the passage of the ice-sheets, rise only a few hundred feet above the surface of the surrounding plateau. The shield slopes towards its centre, which is occupied by the shallow Hudson Bay.

Along the southern margin of the Canadian Shield lie areas of lower land, floored in general with younger rocks and covered with a deeper and richer soil than the uplands of the Shield. The Lakes Peninsula, which projects between Lake Huron on the one side and Lakes Ontario and Erie on the other, and constitutes the most southerly extremity of Canada, is such an area. It is a low, rolling plain, much of it thickly covered with glacial deposits. Moraines and eskers wind across a drift-covered surface. Around the margins are clay deposits, left in post-glacial times when the Great Lakes were more extensive than they are to-day. The dominant relief feature of the Lakes Peninsula is the Niagara escarpment. This scarp resembles in its structural features the scarps of lowland England. It lies across the peninsula from south-east to north-west. It separates Lake Erie from Lake Ontario and gives rise to the waterfalls, whose name it bears. On the other side it extends into Lake Huron as a peninsula and chain of islands, and is continued into Upper Michigan.

The St. Lawrence lowlands stretch north-eastwards from Lake Ontario, narrowing gradually as the highlands of the Shield approach the uplands of New England. Near the outlet of Lake Ontario the plain is about a hundred miles wide. Near Montreal it has been reduced to

about sixty, and near Quebec it is reduced to a narrow bench or platform on the northern shore of the St. Lawrence estuary and a rather
wider belt on the southern. Like the Lakes Peninsula, these lowlands
are also covered with glacial deposits, which have in turn been hidden
by marine deposits laid down during the period of high sea level which
followed the retreat of the ice. The level surface of these lowlands is

Fig. 40. EASTERN CANADA: RELIEF REGIONS

broken to the east of Montreal by the group of isolated volcanic masses
—the Monteregian Hills.

To the south-east of the St. Lawrence Valley are the uplands that
continue northwards and north-eastwards from the hills of New England. These are lower and more often interrupted by expanses of flat
or rolling land than are their counterparts in the United States, but
they culminate nevertheless in the rugged Shickshock Mountains of the
Gaspé Peninsula.

On the south-eastern side of this mountainous belt are the lowlands of the Canadian Maritime Provinces, a continuation of the plains of Maine. The province of New Brunswick is a rolling plain, rising inland to a plateau which forms part of the Appalachian system. The lower ground is thickly mantled with glacial deposits and with silts similar to the clay deposits of the St. Lawrence lowlands. The plain of New Brunswick is continued eastwards in the low, irregular peninsula of Nova Scotia. Close offshore are the islands of Cape Breton and Prince Edward and, further into the Gulf of St. Lawrence, the low, flat island of Anticosti, the rocks and reefs of the Magdalen Islands and of St. Pierre and Miquelon; and, beyond these, is the larger and more rugged island of Newfoundland.

To the north of the Canadian Shield is a vast archipelago of islands, large and small, which probably represent a fractured extension of the Shield. They are still largely unexplored. Some are very mountainous; several have extensive ice-sheets, all are treeless wastes without settled inhabitants and incapable of agricultural development.

The whole of this region, even the peninsulas and islands around the mouth of the St. Lawrence, has a harsh climate. Winters are long and cold, and snowfall is heavy and lies far into the spring. The summers are cool and short. Long before the end of August the maples along the river are beginning to turn yellow, and snow still covers the Laurentides when in the Mid-West the spring flowers are beginning to wilt in the heat of early summer. The January temperatures in the Lakes Peninsulas, the Maritime Provinces, and Newfoundland range from an average of 15 degrees to one of 25 degrees. The St. Lawrence valley is colder, and the larger part of the Laurentian Shield has average temperatures in January from zero to –25 degrees. Only in the Lakes Peninsula are the summers warm. Elsewhere they are at best cool. The total precipitation is light in all parts except the coastal regions of the Maritime Provinces and of Newfoundland. Snowfall is heavy along the St. Lawrence Valley and in Newfoundland, and large areas have an annual total of over 100 inches of snow.

The soils of eastern Canada are such as would be expected with a climate of such severity. On the Shield are large areas of bare rock where no soil has yet formed since the last glacial period. Between these are hollows in which bog has developed. Elsewhere the soil is strongly podsolized. The small amount of humus contributed by the mainly coniferous vegetation is quickly leached away. Along the St. Lawrence Valley and in the Lakes Peninsula the more vigorous growth of plants, combined with the annual leaf-fall, contributes more humus to the soil;

though still strongly leached, it is more brown than grey, more akin to the soils of the Mid-West than to those of the Shield.

When white men first arrived, the land of eastern Canada was densely forested. Over the Shield were coniferous forests—spruce and pine—with a few hardy deciduous trees like the birch, the willow and the poplar. Northwards, this passed through forests of dwarfed trees into the barren tundra. Along the St. Lawrence Valley, in the Maritime Provinces and the Lakes Peninsula, were hardwood forests: maple, poplar, elm, oak and, making its rare appearance in sheltered spots, the beech. Even here the coniferous trees were dominant on higher ground and on areas where the quality of the soil deteriorated.

THE BOUNDARY OF EASTERN CANADA. The United States meets Canada along a boundary of 3,987 miles of which 2,198.2, roughly 55 per cent, is made up of rivers and lakes. No attempt was made to delimit the boundary until, in 1783, the United States achieved independence. By the terms of the Treaty of Paris of that year, the United States and Great Britain:

> agreed and declared, that following are and shall be their Boundaries, viz. From the North West Angle of Nova Scotia, viz. That Angle which is formed by a line drawn due North from the Source of Saint Croix River to the Highlands along the said Highlands which divide those Rivers that empty themselves into the River St. Lawrence, from those which fall into the Atlantic Ocean, to the Northwestern-most Head of Connecticut River: Thence down along the middle of that River to the forty-fifth Degree of North Latitude; From thence by a Line due West on said Latitude until it strikes the River Iroquois or Cataraquy; Thence along the middle of said River into Lake Ontario; through the Middle of said Lake until it strikes the Communication by water between that Lake and Lake Erie; Thence along the middle of said Communication into Lake Erie; through the middle of said Lake, until it arrives at the Water Communication between that Lake and Lake Huron; Thence along the middle of said Water Communication into Lake Huron, thence through the middle of said Lake to the Water Communication between that Lake and Lake Superior, thence through Lake Superior Northwards to the Isles Royal and Phelipeaux to the Long Lake; Thence through the Middle of said Long-Lake, and the Water Communication between it and the Lake of the Woods, to the said Lake of the Woods. . . .[1]

But the delimitation of a boundary is no better than the maps on which it is based. Mitchell's map of North America, which was used at

[1] H. Miller, *Treaties and Other International Acts of the United States of America* (U.S. Govt. Printer, 1931), pp. 152-3.

the Paris Conference of 1783, was highly inaccurate and misleading. An immense number of commissions and agreements, between 1794 and 1925, have been necessary to amend and explain the treaty of 1783.[1] As now defined and delimited, the boundary between the United States and Canada passes between the islands of Passamaquoddy Bay, at the entrance to the Bay of Fundy, and then follows the St. Croix River to its source. It is continued northwards by straight line to the St. John River, which is followed for a distance. The boundary then conforms approximately with the divide between the St. Lawrence drainage and the streams that flow to the Atlantic Ocean, as far south as the 45th parallel of latitude. The boundary then follows the parallel until it meets the St. Lawrence. From this point to the north-western shore of Lake Superior the boundary keeps either to the middle of the rivers or follows approximately the middle line of the lakes. The expression "middle of the lake", which occurs several times in the treaty of 1783, is vague, and the delimitation of the boundary within the water area has been the subject of prolonged though friendly discussion between the two countries.

West of Lake Superior, the delimitation proposed in 1783 proved to be meaningless when demarcation was undertaken. The "Long Lake" does not exist and the Lake of the Woods has no water connection with Lake Superior. The boundary now follows lakes and rivers roughly in the sense indicated in the treaty.

THE GROWTH OF THE DOMINION. We have already seen how, in the sixteenth and seventeenth centuries, the French explored and settled the St. Lawrence Valley. While the *coureurs de bois* were travelling through the northern forests and discovering the portages that led to the Mississippi and Ohio, English and Scottish settlers were establishing themselves in Nova Scotia which thus received its name of "New Scotland". The territory now known as the Maritime Provinces thus acquired its predominantly British character.

The English had reached the island of Newfoundland before the end of the fifteenth century, and through the sixteenth were developing its fisheries. In this they were joined by the Portuguese and the French. When, in 1583, Sir Humphrey Gilbert visited Newfoundland and annexed it to the British crown, he found it "populous and frequented" with fishermen of all nations. The island itself remained in British hands, but the numerous foreign fishermen retained the right to land

---

[1] These are listed in S. W. Boggs, *International Boundaries* (New York, 1940), pp. 219–36.

on its shores and dry their cod fish, and the French[1] ultimately acquired the group of eight small islands commonly known as St. Pierre and Miquelon for this purpose.

But, with these exceptions, the territory of modern Canada long remained predominantly French in settlement and speech. French Canada was essentially the St. Lawrence Valley, where the population was gathered in the three centres, now the chief cities of Quebec—Montreal, Quebec and Three Rivers. The homesteads of the French peasant farmers lay along the river banks; their holdings—long, narrow strips of land—reached back from the water into the forest. At intervals there was a village, with a priest and a church. Outside the three cities already mentioned, society was predominantly rural and agricultural. French immigration practically ceased about 1670, when there was a French population of about 6,700. In the mid-eighteenth century, when French rule ended, there were about 65,000 French settlers in Canada, descended from the immigrants of over a century earlier.

In 1759 the English captured Quebec and ended the period of French rule. Four years later Canada was ceded to England. Hitherto Englishmen in Canada had been limited to the few settlers in the present Maritime Provinces and the even fewer fur hunters and traders who worked through the northern forests in the service of the Hudson's Bay Company. But after 1763, English-speaking settlers began to move into Canada, some from England and some from the American colonies to the south. During the American Revolution the "Loyalists" moved into Canada.

Most English-speaking settlers came to "Upper" Canada, the part of the St. Lawrence Valley that lay above or south-west of Montreal. The Ottawa River came to separate the predominantly French from the mainly English-settled areas and subsequently formed the boundary between the provinces of Quebec and Ontario. In Ontario the English-speaking settlers constituted a compact body of people whose loyalty to the English crown was increased rather than diminished by the proximity of the French-speaking Canadians in Lower Canada, between them and the Atlantic Ocean.

The French of Lower Canada constituted a serious problem for the British Government. They spoke French in an English-speaking continent; they were Roman Catholic, whereas the great majority of the English settlers were Protestant. They maintained their French law and

---

[1] This right was confirmed in the Treaty of Utrecht (1713). In 1783, the islands of St. Pierre and Miquelon, which had been used for this purpose, were ceded to France by Great Britain.

their French social institutions. They were feudal, almost medieval, in their view of society, whereas the English belonged to the trading, progressive middle class. By the Quebec Act of 1774, Great Britain guaranteed the continuance of most of these institutions. They also ensured at least the neutrality of their French Canadian subjects in the war which began two years later between Great Britain and her American colonies. In 1791, both Upper, or English, and Lower, or French, Canada obtained legislative councils of their own. In most respects the two colonies were administered separately from one another and also from the colonies in the Maritime Provinces. The most fruitful source of disagreement between Upper and Lower Canada arose from the location of Lower Canada astride the only important commercial route leading to Upper—the River St. Lawrence.

In the middle of the nineteenth century Canada was made up of Upper and Lower Canada, now governed as a unit, and the three Maritime provinces of New Brunswick, Nova Scotia and Prince Edward Island. The island of Newfoundland was distinct from Canada. West of Upper Canada lay the Prairies and the Rockies, across which the 49th Parallel separated Canada from the United States.

Population in all parts of Canada was increasing steadily. That of Upper Canada had, with the influx of English and Irish settlers in the 1840's and 1850's begun to exceed that in Lower Canada. The Maritime Provinces were smaller, but their geographical similarity and their close proximity to one another were leading to proposals to federate into a single state. No railroad linked them with Lower Canada, and during the winter months, when ice prevented navigation on the St. Lawrence, they were completely cut off from Quebec.

This threatened division into the St. Lawrence Valley and the Maritime colonies was happily averted. The railroad from Halifax, Nova Scotia, to Quebec, a project described in 1847 as "second in importance to none . . . in any portion of the British Dominions", was proposed and became a condition of federation. The construction of such a railroad was clearly imminent when the Maritime Provinces agreed to federation with the "two Canadas".

In 1867 the Dominion of Canada came into being. It consisted of Lower and Upper Canada or, as they were now more often called, Quebec and Ontario, with the provinces of New Brunswick and Nova Scotia. Prince Edward Island stood out until 1873, and Newfoundland refused to become part of Canada.

At this time the prairies of present-day Manitoba were thinly settled, but further to the west there were practically no permanent English

AN FRANCISCO. *The photograph was taken facing north. In the middle distance is the en Gate with its suspension bridge. In the distance to the left is the Pacific Ocean. To the is San Francisco harbour and the Oakland suspension bridge. The small island is Alcatraz.*
THE SAN BERNARDINO MOUNTAINS OF SOUTHERN CALIFORNIA.

(I) QUEBEC. *The old city lies above the steep north bank of the St. Lawrence River. The Cha...*
Frontenac Hotel is right of centre. To the left are the Heights of Abraham scaled by Wolfe in 1...
(II) MONTREAL. *An aerial view of the city looking east. In the distance can be seen the r...*
water of the Lachine Rapids.

settlers. In 1870, Manitoba became a province of the Canadian Dominion. On the Pacific coast there had for many years been English settlements on Vancouver Island, at Vancouver, and along the lower Fraser River. After 1867, a movement amongst the "overlander" settlers, who had come across the prairies, for admission to the Dominion gained ground. In 1871, British Columbia became a province. One of her conditions of admission was that a railway should be completed across the Prairies and Rockies from the Great Lakes to the Pacific coast. The Canadian Pacific Railroad was completed in 1885.

The Prairie Provinces of Alberta and Saskatchewan were admitted in 1905. The northern boundary of British Columbia and the Prairie Provinces was fixed early in the present century along the 60th parallel of latitude. North of this line the land is largely made up of forest and tundra. Agricultural settlements were regarded as impossible and the population, which was largely engaged in trapping, lumbering and mining was too small for these lands ever to become provinces with the degree of self-government enjoyed by other provinces of the Dominion. They are administered by nominees of the federal government and have not developed any effective organs of local government. They at present comprise the Yukon Territory and the North West Territories, the latter being subdivided for administrative purposes into the three districts of Mackenzie, Keewatin and Franklin.

The last province to be admitted to the Dominion was Newfoundland. Newfoundland makes the proud claim of being Britain's oldest colony. But it was also economically one of the weakest. It had refused partnership in the Dominion in 1867, but in 1948 its people voted by a narrow majority to accept membership of the Dominion of Canada, in which Newfoundland now forms the tenth province.

PROBLEMS OF UNITY. On the map the Dominion of Canada appears as a relatively compact territory. In reality, as we have seen, it is made up of a small number of areas of thicker population separated from one another by areas of very sparse population. We have already seen that there are four such populous areas: the Maritime Provinces, the St. Lawrence Valley and the Ontario Peninsula, the agricultural Prairies of Manitoba and Saskatchewan, and south-western British Columbia.

The main lines of communication are in an east to west direction, with Winnipeg as the mid-continent focus of routes. Railways were of very great significance as factors in both Canadian settlement and Canadian unity. Both the Maritime Provinces and British Columbia only entered the Dominion on the understanding that the construction

M

of a transcontinental railway would be expedited as much as possible.

An elaborate system was necessary in the interests of national unity. It was probably bigger than the economic and transport needs of the country required. A consequence was that the railways were not fully utilized and were not economic. As a result, two important undertakings, the Canadian Northern and the Grand Trunk Pacific failed financially, were amalgamated and operated as the state-owned Canadian National Railroad.

The earlier pattern of settlement of Canada conformed with the agricultural wealth of the country. But the former empty lands are now seen to be rich in minerals. The Canadian Shield is already of great importance as a source of metals, and there is every reason to believe that this importance will increase with the development of iron mines in northern Quebec. This, in turn, is attracting population to these waste areas, and in recent years many small towns have sprung up.

A second source of political weakness in Canada arises from the variety of its immigrant population. Out of a total population in 1941 of 11,506,655, English-speaking Canadians of English origin made up 5,715,904, or 50 per cent. The French-speaking accounted for 3,483,038 or 31 per cent. The remaining 19 per cent were made up of groups, chiefly of European origin, among which the German, Scandinavian, Ukrainian, Jewish, Dutch, Polish and Italian each contributed over 100,000. None of these peoples accounted for more than 4 per cent of the total. The aboriginal Canadian population of Indian and Eskimo numbered only 125,521, 1 per cent of the total. The French Canadians constitute by far the largest, the most concentrated and the most important politically of the groups. Its high birth-rate makes it the most rapidly expanding group.

THE FRENCH-SPEAKING CANADIANS. The earlier tendency was for the population of Canada to form a number of "islands". One of these "islands" is not only remote geographically from the others, but it is also distinct in language and culture. It is that of the French-speaking Canadians. The small colony of about 6,700 French settlers in Canada in about 1670, when French immigration virtually ceased, has multiplied and now numbers about 3,483,000. It derives its culture entirely from the feudal, Catholic France of the pre-Revolutionary era. It remains almost wholly Roman Catholic in faith and French in language.

The role of the Roman Catholic Church in maintaining the individuality of the French Canadians has been of immense importance. It strengthens the family ties and by means of its church schools it insulates them in some degree from the influence of the American and of the English-speaking Canadian. It is the Roman Catholic priest "who, now as in the past, holds them together, physically and morally, and gives them the true conception of their own racial, linguistic and spiritual individuality".[1]

The French settlement area is basically that section of the St. Lawrence Valley from eastern Ontario to northern New Brunswick, where they were settled in the seventeenth century. But the high reproduction rate and the consequent rapid increase in their numbers has led to migration. The French Canadians have moved into the Maritime Provinces where they now constitute over a fifth of the total population. They have settled in the New England States, particularly in Maine. They have pressed up the St. Lawrence Valley west of Montreal. They occur in the Lakes Peninsula of Ontario; they are establishing their little farms along the railways which cross the "Shield" in northern Ontario. They are a small but increasing minority in the Prairie Provinces, and only British Columbia has to-day relatively few French-speaking Canadians.

In origin they were almost exclusively rural; they were "North America's most stable and archaic rural society".[2] The basic geographical division of French Canada is the parish, the small territorial unit upon which the social and religious life of the community is focused, for the parish is in reality a unit for church administration (see p. 174). The parish is an area which supports a church and priest, and the priest is in virtue of his vocation the leader of the parish community, and he is often the intermediary between it and the outside world.

But the agricultural basis of French Canadian society is breaking down. The amount of good agricultural land in Quebec Province is small and is limited to the narrow tract along each side of the St. Lawrence River and its tributaries. Life is hard in the forested hills away from the stream, and some of these frontier communities show signs of declining in importance. The rural and agricultural population of Quebec Province increased by only 29 per cent between 1871 and 1931, but the French Canadian population of greater Montreal increased during the same period by 650 per cent, and that of other urban centres by 403 per cent. The French Canadian population is becoming to an increasing degree an urban and industrial population. The little towns of Quebec are developing manufactures: metal and textile goods,

---

[1] André Siegfried, *Canada* (London, 1949), p. 63.
[2] Everett Cherrington Hughes, *French Canada in Transition* (London and New York, 1946), p. 1.

articles made of wood and paper. But there is no decline in agriculture; only a slower growth than in the past.

Quebec Province is overwhelmingly French Canadian; the other provinces have only small though in places growing French Canadian minorities. The high reproduction rate of the French Canadians suggests that they may before many years have outnumbered the Canadians of English origin. The English Canadians are content to regard Quebec as a French Canadian province, but they like to regard Ontario, British Columbia and the Prairie Provinces as predominantly English. They view with some apprehension the immigration of the French. For their part the French Canadians also have problems. The unity of a closely settled agricultural people is beginning to weaken. They can remain on the land only at the expense of migrating to other parts of the Dominion or to the United States. They can remain in Quebec only at the expense of entering factories, where they come under influences contrary to those of the Roman Catholic priest.

NEWFOUNDLAND. The island of Newfoundland, discovered by the Cabots at the end of the fifteenth century, settled by a small group of English colonists late in the sixteenth, was one of the oldest of Britain's overseas possessions. It was also one of the poorest. It lies at the south of the Gulf of St. Lawrence. The Cabot Strait, some 60 miles wide, separates it from Nova Scotia. The narrow Strait of Belle Isle lies between it and the coast of Labrador. Its rugged and indented coast line encloses 42,734 square miles of forest, lake, bog and bare rock. Structurally the island is a part of the Appalachian—New England system. It is built of rocks palaeozoic and even greater geological age, much folded and now reduced to an undulating tableland, highest in the west, but even here not exceeding 3,000 feet above the sea.

Offshore, to the east and south-east, is the shallowing of the ocean floor known as the Grand Banks. Here the cold water of the Labrador current, which comes south from Greenland and Baffin Land, bearing icebergs, which slowly melt in these lower latitudes, meets the warmer oceanic drift from the south. The warm air is chilled by the cold Arctic stream, and banks of fog are formed. Navigational hazards, already considerable on account of the ice floes that come drifting southwards, are increased many times. In addition to this the fog-bound Banks of Newfoundland are one of the most intensively fished areas of the Atlantic Ocean.

The climate of Newfoundland, very cold and snowy in winter, cool in summer, does not encourage agriculture, and only a minute proportion of the island is under cultivation. Its resources are in its forests and mines and, above all, in the sea around it.

The population of Newfoundland, about 361,416, is scattered around the coast of the island. St. John's, the capital, has about 66,497. There are only two other settlements with over 5,000, and there are some 1,300 other small settlements. Communication between these settlements is made difficult by the climatic conditions and by the utter inadequacy of the roads and railways. These isolated settlements rely almost entirely on shipping to maintain their contact with the outside world.

The fishing industry occupies almost half the employed male population. It is carried on only during the period from March to October or November, but during this period the fishing craft, from small "dories" to large schooners, range from close inshore to the Grand Banks and the coast of Labrador. The cod is the most important fish, but halibut, turbot, lobster and others are taken. Fish is exported, packed in ice, to the mainland, but much of it is salted or dried before being shipped.

Mining is an important industry. On Bell Island, in the southeast of Newfoundland, iron ore is mined and shipped chiefly to Nova Scotia. Output has in recent times averaged about a million tons a year. Copper, lead and zinc are mined in the interior of the island, at Botwood, and fluorspar is also obtained.

The forest industries are second in importance to the fisheries. Much of the softwood forest has been leased to pulp and paper companies. Mills have been established near the coast, and there are no difficulties, except in winter, in the way of the export of the products. Unlike the fisheries, the lumber and pulp industries give employment throughout the year in cutting, logging and transporting the timber. Both mining and lumbering have given rise to small and rough, but permanent, settlements in the interior of the island.

With agricultural activities reduced to negligible proportions, Newfoundland is heavily dependent upon the import of foodstuffs and consumers' goods, and thus upon being able to market its staple products. Until 1934, Newfoundland was a self-governing dominion within the British Commonwealth. The depression, which had begun a few years earlier, had closed the world market to Newfoundland's products. The economic plight of the island was disastrous, and in these conditions the Newfoundlanders exchanged their self-governing status for government by a commission, appointed by the British Government. This episode ended soon after the Second World War; self-government was restored, and soon afterwards the islanders sought and gained admission to the Dominion of Canada as its newest province.

For over half the year Newfoundland is held in the grip of sea ice, which at its greatest extent encloses all except the south coast. The port of St. John's is situated on the most easterly extremity, where the duration of sea ice is relatively short. The navigational dangers of ice and fog have led shipping to avoid as much as possible the seas near Newfoundland. This handicap, however, does not apply to air routes. Newfoundland is the nearest convenient land fall in the American continent for planes flying from western Europe. At Gander, about 120 miles northwest of St. John's, an airfield has been laid out amid the forest, and equipment assembled for the fuelling and repair of the huge transatlantic aircraft, which fly in and out of this clearing in the sub-arctic wilderness with the precision of buses at a city depot.

THE MARITIME PROVINCES. These are the three small provinces lying to the south of the Gulf of St. Lawrence. New Brunswick, a compact rectangular-shaped territory, is an extension of the hills and plains of northern Maine. Nova Scotia is made up of a peninsula of highly irregular form, together with the island of Cape Breton. Prince Edward Island, smallest of the three provinces, is cradled within the incurving shores of the other two.

The provinces make up a region of subdued relief, developed in old and highly folded rocks. The whole area was glaciated and much of the old rock surface is hidden under glacial deposits. Rivers are short and of little value for irrigation. The coast is indented and on many of the inlets, particularly the Bay of Fundy, coastal marshes have formed and are being enclosed and converted to agricultural use. The Bay of Fundy is itself remarkable for the exceptional tidal range—up to 50 feet —which the sea exhibits.

The Maritime Provinces have a climate that is milder than that of Newfoundland. Only the shores of the Gulf of St. Lawrence are held in the grip of sea ice in winter. Most of the coast of Nova Scotia is open, a fact which has led to the development of Halifax as the chief winter port of eastern Canada. Nevertheless, snowfall is heavy and the growing period for crops is very short except near the coast and in the south. The natural vegetation is hardwood forest on the lower ground, mixed and coniferous on the higher. The soil is podsolized and of no great value except in the reclaimed coastal areas.

The population is largely English speaking, and most is of British origin. A few French-speaking colonies survive from the eighteenth century when the region as a whole was disputed between the English settlers of New England and the French settlers of the St. Lawrence

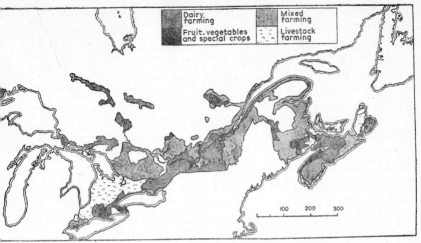

Fig. 41. EASTERN CANADA: VEGETATION AND AGRICULTURE

valley. The Maritime Provinces received a considerable number of the
Loyalists who left the revolting American colonies towards the end of
the eighteenth century. Recently a number of French-speaking
Canadians have moved over from the crowded farms of Quebec.

The Maritime Provinces are predominantly agricultural. The climate
restricts the range of crops grown and limits them to the lower ground.
Mixed farming is most widely practised. Fodder crops and grass grow
well enough to support a dairying industry. Vegetables and potatoes
are grown and locally, as in the Woodstock district of New Brunswick,
are very important. Temperate fruit and vegetables are grown in the
Annapolis Valley of Nova Scotia, which borders the Bay of Fundy. The
cultivation of cereal crops, unable to compete with grain production in
the Prairie provinces, is unimportant.

Forestry and fishing are very much less important than in Newfoundland, but nevertheless, add appreciably to the income of the Maritime Provinces. Much of the area remains forested, and saw mills are
scattered through Nova Scotia and New Brunswick. Nova Scotia is
twice as far from the Grand Banks as the ports of Newfoundland, but
smaller banks, scarcely less productive of fish, are at hand, and there
are a number of fishing ports in Nova Scotia, from which both the
deep-sea and the inshore fisheries are worked.

The mineral industries are relatively important. Most significant are
the coal mines of Nova Scotia. A small coal-field occupies the northern
part of Cape Breton Island, and the coal measures extend out under the
Gulf of St. Lawrence. Coal is also mined in the narrow isthmus by

which the main part of Nova Scotia is joined to the mainland. The
mines of Cape Breton Island to-day produce about 6,200,000 tons of
coal a year; the remaining mines in the Maritime Provinces yield some
650,000. Mining is relatively difficult owing to the thin and folded
nature of the seams and also on account of the extension of the workings
under the sea. The coal is expensive to mine but has the advantage of
nearness to the coast and to cheap sea-borne transport. Coal is distributed to the ports of the St. Lawrence Valley and of Newfoundland,
and there is a considerable utilization by the local railways and industries. Foremost amongst the latter are the iron and steel works at Sydney, on Cape Breton Island, which smelt ore imported from Bell Island
with coke made from the local coal.

Population is scanty in the Maritime Provinces. There are together
only about 1,250,000 people scattered over an area of 50,400 square
miles. Towns are few and small and the largest, Halifax in Nova Scotia,
has only 70,488 people. The iron-smelting centre of Sydney is a small
town of 31,317 people. Halifax lies on a wide, deep, fjord-like opening
on the Nova Scotian coast. Not only is its harbour naturally protected;
it is ice-free in winter, and at this season of the year dominates the
Atlantic trade of Canada.

ST. LAWRENCE VALLEY. The Gulf of St. Lawrence, narrowing to
the estuary and then to the river, led the early explorers and settlers
inland. The St. Lawrence lowlands opened before them, drawing
them deeper into a region of less rugged climate and gentle relief. The
French settled on the shores of the St. Lawrence River, laying out their
villages and farms along the waterfront. The pattern of settlement and
field is still basically that which was laid down by the French settlers in
the sixteenth and seventeenth centuries. The farm is a long strip of
land, reaching from its narrow frontage on the river, where is the farm-
house and sometimes a small landing stage, back across the level land
with its cultivated fields to the wooded hills beyond. At intervals one
sees the small clustered village, not laid out in squares like the American, but an irregular huddle of houses and farm buildings gathered
around the steeple of the village church, just as in France. Movement
between these settlements has always been as much by water as by land.
Today a road network is spread over the St. Lawrence lowlands, linking
the villages and farms with the cities. Nevertheless, the world of the
French-speaking Canadians lies apart from the main stream of American
and Canadian life. Their villages are more nearly self-sufficing than any
other white settlements of the continent, and traditional patterns of be-

haviour are more firmly established and less vulnerable than elsewhere.

Through this French-settled region the St. Lawrence River flows a magnificent navigable highway, over a mile in width, broadening in places to as much as ten miles. Above Montreal the river is obstructed by rocky bars which lie across the stream and create rapids. The St. Lawrence is joined by a number of large tributaries which each open a route into the hills on each side. The Saguenay River rises deep within the Shield and joins the river about 120 miles below Quebec. Almost opposite Quebec is the mouth of the Chaudière, which rises on the border of Maine. A little below Montreal, the Richelieu River comes in from New York State, and with its valley completes the low-level routeway from New York to Montreal. The Ottawa River, rising on the

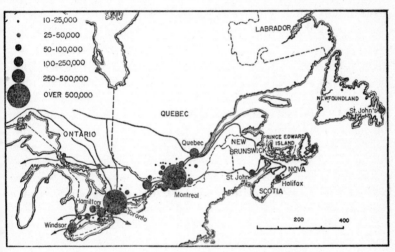

Fig. 42. EASTERN CANADA: CITIES AND TRANSPORT

southern margin of the Shield, joins the river a short distance above Montreal. Many other streams tumble down from the hills on either side, bearing timber or generating power for the mills and factories of Quebec.

The city of Quebec lies on the northern shore of the St. Lawrence, where the estuary narrows to the river. As every history student knows, the old French city lay on the heights overlooking the river and protected on the north by the deep valley of the little St. Charles River, whose mouth formed the harbour. The city now covers a larger area than when General Wolfe scaled the cliffs to reach the Heights of Abraham. There are now about 161,500 people instead of the few hundreds of the mid-eighteenth century. Docks and railway yards have been built on the St. Charles. Cunard liners now tie up where Wolfe's soldiers must have stepped ashore from their flotilla of row-boats. A huge hotel has been built on the edge of Montcalm's citadel. But despite these changes, Quebec retains the atmosphere of colonial days more completely than any other Canadian—perhaps any American—city. The walls of the old city in part remain, encircling the narrow winding streets, the steep valleys descending to the St. Lawrence or the St. Charles; the streets of shuttered houses which, if not typically French, are at least more European than American. The Heights of Abraham are still a breezy, grassy common, hemmed in now by buildings, but still commanding a view—one of the most impressive in the continent—northwards over the Laurentides and the estuary, southwards over the river and valley of the St. Lawrence.

Montreal has none of the quaintness and the preoccupation with the past that are so attractive in Quebec. Between the junctions of the Ottawa River and Richelieu River with the St. Lawrence is a group of islands. The river narrows and is obstructed by rapids which formerly set a limit to navigation. Rising from the longest of these is the hill—Mont Réal or Mount Royal—described by Cartier. On the eastern side of this hill, between it and the river, there grew up the settlement of Montreal. Montreal had advantages denied to Quebec. It lay at the limit of ocean navigation. Valleys converged on it from the west, south-west and south. It became the starting point of expeditions to the West, the headquarters of the French trappers and traders and, in later years, the starting point of the transcontinental railways.

Two-thirds of the population of Montreal is of French origin, and other groups of non-English origin are more important here than in any other Canadian city. In its cosmopolitan nature Montreal resembles the great American industrial cities. Montreal is primarily a commercial city, with extensive docks along the eastern side of the island. Its important role as a banking and financial centre derives from its commercial importance. Its factories make paper, mill flour, refine sugar, and manufacture textiles.

Other cities of the St. Lawrence Valley are dwarfed by Quebec and Montreal. But they are numerous, and many have important factory industries. Sorel (14,961) is a shipbuilding centre; St. Hyacinthe (20,236) and Drummondville (14,341) have textile industries; Three Rivers (45,708) has pulp and paper factories; Sherbrooke (49,737) has engineering and textile industries. In addition to the industrial towns are the mining centres of Thetford Mines and neighbouring communities, which produce a very large proportion, about 75 per cent, of the world's asbestos.

THE LAKES PENINSULA OF ONTARIO. The Great Lakes had a complex history during glacial and pre-glacial times. As the ice-sheet retreated, marginal lakes, very much more extensive than the present lake system, were formed. As the land surface gradually recovered from its depression under the weight of the ice, the water bodies contracted to their present dimensions. In the course of this development, however, the water took many short-cuts on its way to the ocean. One of these was the wide valley now occupied by the diminutive Mohawk River in New York State. At one phase in the retreat of the ice the water made its way by this route to the Hudson River. More important to us now are the routes which it took from the upper lakes to the lower. It occupied in succession the depression which lies between Georgian Bay and the western end of Lake Ontario and the North Bay—Ottawa River route before, at last, variations in the land and water levels brought the waters of Lake Huron to their present outlet through the St. Clair and Detroit Rivers to Lake Erie.

The Lakes Peninsula has emerged from these changes in shape somewhat like an arrow-head with conspicuous barbs. These "barbs" are the Niagara Peninsula on the east and that which separates Georgian Bay from Lake Huron on the north. These excrescences are formed by the outcrop of the Niagara limestone which here forms a scarp, many hundreds of feet high in most places and facing north or north-east. The falls from which the scarp is named occur where the drainage of Lake Erie drops 327 feet to the lower level of Lake Ontario.

The many changes both of drainage and of lake level have led to the deposition of large areas of lacustrine clays, which to-day support good quality farming. But widespread beds of sand were also laid down. These are infertile and, unless they have been forested, are liable to blow.

The climate improves rapidly as the peninsula is followed from its base against the Canadian Shield to its furthermost tip, where it looks across the river to Detroit. The growing season is on average seventy days longer at one extremity than at the other, and the January temperature no less than 17 degrees higher.

The whole region was formerly forested. In the extreme south-west the forests were of broad-leaved trees amongst which were species common in the Mid-West. But north-eastwards the more tender species died away and conifers made their appearance. Near the margin of

the Shield coniferous trees took over and the broad-leaved were represented only by the hardy birch, poplar and an occasional maple.

Most of this forest has now been cleared and the Lakes Peninsula is
very largely under cultivation. Dairy and mixed farming predominates.
Summers are hot enough for corn to be an important crop. Tobacco
and fodder crops are grown. Close to the lakes, where the danger of late
frosts is reduced to a minimum, early vegetables are grown and fruit,
including the grape vine and peaches, is able to ripen.

But it is as an industrial region that the Lakes Peninsula is most
noted. There are countless factories which process or preserve the
vegetable products of the region: mills producing wood pulp and paper,
dairies and canneries for fruit and vegetables. Though the region
lacks the raw materials of the iron industry, smelting and steel-making
are established at Hamilton. Motor cars are built at Windsor, across
the river from Detroit. Engineering, iron founding and the construction
of agricultural equipment and machines of every kind is carried on at
numerous centres.

Toronto. Foremost amongst the industrial cities of Ontario is Toronto
(673,104). The city was established late in the eighteenth century on the
north shore of Lake Ontario, where a small bay gave some shelter to
shipping. Inland from the city was good farmland and only seventy-one
miles away was the head of Georgian Bay. In its rectilinear planning
and its tall buildings Toronto resembles the great American cities more
nearly than any other in Canada. It is a city of great commercial significance, a centre of banking and of stock exchange activities. It has also
a wide range of manufacturing industries which include mechanical
and electrical engineering, the textile and clothing industries, food
processing and oil refining.

Hamilton (192,125), at the western end of Lake Ontario, is second in
size to Toronto. It is a port with a large sheltered harbour formed at the
most westerly extremity of Lake Ontario by an enclosing bar of sand
and shingle. Its industrial importance derives mainly from its blast
furnace and steel works, the most important in Canada, which are well
placed to receive by water the coal of Pennsylvania and the iron ore of
the upper Great Lakes.

Ottawa (188,665) is third in size amongst the cities of Lower Ontario,
but, unlike the others, its importance is not primarily industrial. It was
only a small settlement when in 1867 it was chosen as capital of the
newly formed federal Dominion of Canada. Its function has remained

primarily governmental, resembling Washington in the United States and Canberra in Australia. Even its industries, such as printing and publishing, are associated with the function of government.

London (92,789), midway between Toronto and the United States border at Detroit, is the commercial centre of the more westerly part of the Lakes Peninsula, and has metallurgical and engineering industries.

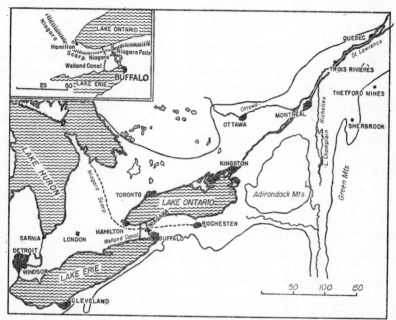

Fig. 43. THE LAKES PENINSULA OF ONTARIO

Windsor (120,532) spreads along the eastern or Canadian shore of the Detroit River. In its industrial structure it is a smaller replica of Detroit, and its largest industry is the making of automobiles. Other industries include engineering and the manufacture of chemicals. There can be no doubt that it is the proximity of Detroit that is in the main responsible for the industrial development of Windsor.

All the industrial cities of Lower Ontario lie on or very close to the Great Lakes, and depend in some degree on water transport for the supply of their raw materials and the carriage of their manufactured products. The Great Lakes have, in the past, constituted a self-contained system, open for navigation during half or two-thirds of the year.

The Welland Canal was enlarged in 1931 to circumvent the only major obstacle to navigation, the Niagara Falls. The waterway between Lake Superior and Lake Huron has been improved by the construction of locks at Saulte Saint Marie. But access to the ocean from the Great Lakes has been impeded by the shallows and rapids that occur along the St. Lawrence River from its outlet at Kingston down to Montreal. A number of canals—no less than six of them, with a combined length of 47 miles—have been constructed to avoid the rapids, but they are too shallow to take any except the smallest ocean freighters. Furthermore, some of the Great Lakes freighters are too large to descend the river.

The present Welland Canal was conceived as part of a Great Lakes-St. Lawrence waterway, which would permit most ocean-going vessels to sail inland to the head of Lake Superior. Attempts to secure agreement between the Canadian and United States governments to canalize the international section of the river—which happens also to be the section most difficult to navigate—ran into opposition in the American Senate. In recent years this opposition, though still vociferous, is much weaker, and in 1953 a tentative agreement was reached for the joint construction of dams and power-stations and the joint operation of a navigable waterway conforming with the size of the Welland and Sault Sainte Marie locks.

The Canadian Shield. The rounded summits of the Laurentides overlook the St. Lawrence estuary. Further south they retreat from the river, leaving a broad belt of lowland along the river. But the margin of the Shield is everywhere abrupt as the pre-Cambrian schists and gneisses emerge from their cover of younger beds. It cuts across the base of the Lakes Peninsula, separating flat and undulating land from the "Rock Knobs" of the Shield, mixed from coniferous woodland and crop land from forest. Westwards the margin continues along the northern shores of Lakes Huron and Superior, encloses a lobe which stretches into the United States, and then moves north-westwards to the Arctic.

The surface of the Shield is undulating. Its hollows are occupied by lakes or peat bogs. A multitude of small streams wind across it, collecting the drainage of the thousands of lakes, until they drop steeply from the edge of the Shield to the lower land to the south and west or to the sea. The even discharge from the lakes of the plateau, interrupted only by the winter freeze, has been admirably suited to the development of hydro-electric power, and a multitude of generating stations has been built close to the edge of the Shield.

The Shield is mainly under forest, which passes northwards into tundra. The forests are relatively easily reached from the St. Lawrence and Ottawa Rivers and from the northern shore of the Great Lakes. The more southerly parts of the Shield have thus become a highly important source of softwood lumber. Sawmills, powered with electricity from the nearby generating stations, occur along the margin of the Shield and on the larger rivers, such as the Saguenay and St. Maurice, which descend from it.

The soil of the Shield is too poor and the climate too severe for agriculture to be important. Nevertheless, mixed farming and cattle raising are practised at a few places deep within its borders. At certain stages in the retreat of the ice shallow lakes were formed along its margin. In these clay and sand accumulated, giving rise to clay belts. Such a belt encloses the Saguenay River and Lake St. John. A more extensive clay belt lies from east to west in Quebec, approximately along the route of the Canadian National Railroad, for a distance of about 400 miles. Other similar but smaller belts of clay lie around Lake Timiskaming, near Sudbury and along the north shore of Lake Huron. The soil is heavy and lacking in humus, and the growing season is short—as little as ninety days in parts of the main clay belt. But draining and the application of large quantities of lime and organic manure have made considerable areas of the clay cultivable. Hay, the more hardy cereals, such as oats and barley, and root and fodder crops are grown.

The Shield has a small population of lumbermen and fur trappers. To these have been added in recent years a growing number of miners, who settle in large and relatively permanent colonies. The Shield is richly mineralized and mining is, after lumbering, the chief source of income. Most of the metalliferous mines occur in the south and southwest of the Shield. Gold and nickel are, in terms of value, the most important minerals. There are many centres of gold mining, most of them remote from railways. Nickel production, however, is concentrated in the Sudbury district, to the north of Georgian Bay. This area has long been the world's foremost source of nickel, and it now contributes about 95 per cent of the world's production. Most of the mines and smelters are owned by the International Nickel Company. North of Sudbury is the rich mining area of Noranda and Kirkland Lake, where important quantities of copper and zinc are mined. The town of Cobalt was formerly a centre for the mining of the mineral of the same name. The production of cobalt has declined in the face of cheaper production in Africa, but silver has become an important product of the Cobalt mines.

Iron ore has not hitherto been an important product of the Shield, at least within the limits of the Dominion of Canada. Most of the deposits around the head of Lake Superior lie on the United States side of the boundary. Recently, however, deposits, apparently of very great size, have been located on the border of the Province of Quebec and Labrador, between the Gulf of St. Lawrence and Ungava Bay. A railway has been constructed from the Gulf of St. Lawrence inland for over 300 miles to the Knob Lake mining area. The opening up of this ore-field, coupled with the completion of the St. Lawrence seaway, is likely to give a new lease of life to the iron-smelting industry of the Great Lakes, threatened by the imminent exhaustion of the ore deposits near Lake Superior.

AGARA FALLS: (1) ONE OF THE POWER STATIONS. *The pipes which deliver the water to the turbines can be clearly seen.*

) HORSESHOE FALLS. *The Niagara River drops 167 feet. On the extreme right can be seen in-take of one of the hydro-electric plants.*

(I) LAKE OKANOGAN, BRITISH COLUMBIA. *This lake lies between the Rocky Mounta* *and the Coast Range. It is drained by the Okanogan River, which joins the Columbia Ri* (II) TRAIL RIDERS NEAR BANFF, ALBERTA. *This is almost the only means of travelling a* *carrying heavy goods in areas untouched by the railway.*

— 13 —

Canada: The West

THE POLITICAL BOUNDARY. Great Britain's treaty of peace with the American colonies in 1783 provided for a political boundary between the United States and the territories remaining under British rule. After following the St. Lawrence River and the middle of each of the Great Lakes, except Lake Michigan, it was, as we have seen, made to follow rivers and lakes whose existence, even less their correct geographical form, was barely known to the negotiators, until it reached the north-west corner of the Lake of the Woods.

The territory west of the Mississippi was at this time French. Its purchase by the United States in 1803 raised in an acute form the problem of deciding how the boundary was to continue from the agreed point on the shore of the Lake of the Woods.

By an agreement of 1818 between Great Britain and the United States, the boundary between Canada and the States was delimited as the 49th Parallel from the Lake of the Woods westwards to the Stony (i.e. Rocky) Mountains. The boundary in the immediate vicinity of the Lake of the woods is an almost grotesque example of the consequences of delimitation without maps. The 49th Parallel was later extended as the boundary between western Canada and the Oregon Territory as far as the Strait of Georgia. The boundary within the Strait of Georgia and the Strait of Juan de Fuca was the subject of subsequent arbitration.

Much has been written on the subject of the "unguarded frontier" between Canada and the United States; it has been commended for "its striking simplicity, apparent artificiality, and long tranquillity". in point of fact, the boundary is clearly demarcated, and is patrolled in order to check smuggling. Through the forested country in which lies the western section of the boundary, a broad avenue is kept clear on each side of the boundary line. Owing to errors in the original survey and demarcation, the boundary is rarely actually on the 49th Parallel.

It is usually a short distance either to the north or south. On balance, neither side has gained or lost a great deal as a result of these errors, and it would require a large-scale map to show the departure of the present boundary from the correctly drawn parallel. Such detail has not affected the relations of the two countries.

Difficulties of a different kind are, however, raised. An important matter is water supply in the prairie provinces. Rivers flow across the boundary, the Milk River flows from Montana into the Canadian pro- vince of Alberta and back again into Montana. The Red River flows from North Dakota into Manitoba. In the mountain section, almost all the rivers flow across the boundary. But the difficulties of river control and problems of irrigation are never so great that they cannot be solved amicably. The boundary has the great advantage of having been established before the settlers came, and they adjusted themselves to a boundary already in existence. The differences, secondly, between the peoples who live on each side of the boundary are slight, their problems and their outlook are similar. "The cultural dissimilarities which exist between Canadians and Americans in the zone of the forty- ninth parallel are probably the least that can maintain national separa- tion."[1]

In this chapter we are concerned with a very much larger extent of territory than in the last. Not only have we the western half of the Shield, similar to but less accessible than the eastern; we have the Prairies, the Rocky Mountains and the fiord-coast of British Columbia. The 60th parallel is a convenient if arbitrary northern limit for the territory considered in this chapter. It is the boundary of the provinces of Manitoba, Saskatchewan, Alberta and British Columbia. North of it the Yukon and the North-West Territories may be described as Arctic and left until the next chapter.

Considerably over half the area now under discussion belongs to the Canadian Shield. The remainder is sharply divisible into two contrasted regions: the Prairies and the Rocky Mountains.

THE CANADIAN SHIELD. The approximate margin of the Shield on the west is marked out by a chain of lakes which mostly occupy hollows excavated in the softer rocks which enclose the Shield. These lakes in- clude the Lakes of the Woods, Lake Winnipeg, a series of small lakes in central Saskatchewan and then Lake Athabasca and the Great Slave Lake. The margin of the Shield is not marked on this side by any conspicuous land forms. The land surface slopes gently and inconspicu-

---

[1] S. B. Jones, in *Geographical Journal*, LXXXIX (1937), p. 439.

ously towards Hudson Bay and James Bay, and is coursed by un-counted numbers of rivers. These rivers mostly flow to the north, to a sea which is frozen and inaccessible for much of the year. They are of little value in transporting the products of the forests and mines, and are of no great value for travel. This is one reason why the western part of the Shield is less developed than the eastern. Nevertheless, mines have been established. Flin Flon, north-west of Lake Winnipeg, is a source of copper, silver, zinc and gold as well as of other minerals. And the Hudson Bay is reached by a few ships which make the journey during the short "open" season in the Hudson Strait. The port of Churchill, at the mouth of the Churchill River, is open for about four months in the year. It has been linked with the Prairies by a railway, and now exports part of the Canadian wheat crop.

The Churchill and Nelson Rivers are of great length, and, if har-nessed, could become important sources of hydro-electric power. At present very little has been done to develop power along the western edge of the Shield.

THE PRAIRIES. Between the Shield and the foothills of the Rocky Mountains is a belt of flat country which rises westwards in a series of steps. Along the United States boundary it is about 750 miles in width. At a latitude of 60 degrees its breadth is diminished to less than 500 miles.

Against the margin of the Shield is a narrow belt of primary rocks. To the west these are overlaid by secondary rocks, chiefly shales inter-bedded with large deposits of coal.

Topographically considered, the Prairies constitute three huge steps or platforms, ranging from 1,000 feet to 3,000 feet above sea level. The lowermost and also the smallest is little more than the valley of the Red River. It is a level, silt-covered plain, drained on the south by the Red River and its tributary the Assiniboine, and in the north by the Saskatchewan River. Lake Winnipeg, into which these rivers flow, is only the shrunken remnant of a large lake, given retrospectively the name of Lake Agassiz, which developed here during the retreat of the ice. Lacustrine deposits were laid down on the lake floor, covering both parts of the Shield and the primary beds along its western edge. The contraction of the former lake has left its level floor, thickly covered with fertile clays and silts, to form one of the most valuable agricul-tural regions of Canada. This, the lowest prairie step, is bounded on the west by a series of hills which, by their contrast with the level Prairie from which they rise, have earned the title of "mountains":

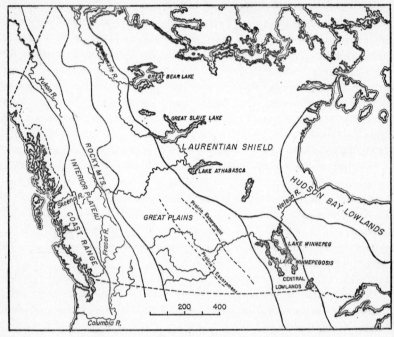

Fig. 44. THE CANADIAN WEST: RELIEF REGIONS

Riding Mountain, Duck Mountain, Porcupine Mountain. In reality
these are no more than the eroded scarps formed by the westward dipping secondary beds.

West of these hills is the second Prairie step, in general about 1,000
feet higher than the first, though more dissected by rivers. It is a rolling
country, broken by isolated hills. It narrows towards the north and is
finally pinched out between the Shield and the third and highest Prairie
step. This last is the most extensive of the three. Like the second it is
bordered on the east by a broken and wind-eroded scarp, which develops here and there into hills of considerable proportions, such as the
Caribou Mountains of northern Alberta. The third step rises from
about 2,000 feet along its scarped edge to about 4,000 feet, at which
height the mountains rise abruptly.

Throughout the Prairies, the climate is severe. The mildest conditions are experienced along the foot of the Rocky Mountains in southern
Alberta. Here January averages rise as high as 15 degrees, but they
quickly fall off to the north and east. Winnipeg has a January average
near zero, and at Churchill, on Hudson Bay, the average falls to 20

degrees below zero. Summers are cool: 65 to 70 degrees in the south in July; below 55 degrees in the north. The relative warmth of winter in the plains of southern Alberta is due to the "chinook", a warm wind of the "fohn" type, which at intervals blows across the mountains from the Pacific.

THE AGRICULTURE OF THE PRAIRIES. The growing season is short: but little over a hundred days in the year in the south, and less than seventy in the north. Winters are shorter close to the Rockies than further to the east, and it is not surprising that agriculture, in its attempts to spread northwards, has made most progress along the foot of the mountains.

The rainfall is low throughout the Prairie provinces. In the east it is little more than 20 inches a year, and at its dryest it is less than 15 inches. Throughout the region evaporation exceeds rainfall. Drought conditions combine with the short growing season to restrict agriculture.

The soils, however, are good. The low rainfall and the high evaporation prevents leaching. Humus decays slowly during the long winters, and its concentration at the surface gives a rich black chernozem in the most favoured areas. Black earths form a semi-circular band, reaching from Winnipeg, through Edmonton to Calgary. On its inner, or southern side, low rainfall restricts plant growth and with it the formation of humus. Outside the belt of black earths come grey forest soils; the greater humidity has led to some degree of leaching and podsolization.

Before the coming of white settlers, the black earth supported a cover of tall prairie grass. On their drier margin was short grass. To the north was a mixed belt where the grassland merged into the forest, and beyond it unbroken stands of coniferous trees and muskeg.

The settled and improved lands of the Prairies form a triangle, its apex in the south-east, near the Lake of the Woods, its base along the Rocky Mountain foothills. Its boundary on the north is formed by the margin of the Shield and by the limit of the coniferous forest with its poorer soils. This triangle of good land was entered by a kind of gateway, between the southern end of Lake Winnipeg and the United States border. Here, on the Red River, was established the city of Winnipeg, and from Winnipeg the westward routes fanned out over the Prairie.

The earliest agricultural land use was ranching. As this pressed westward across the Prairie, it was followed in the east by wheat growing. At the turn of the century the Red River plains of Manitoba were a sea of wheat. Now wheat has moved westward, curving through the black earth Prairie towards the Rocky Mountains. Wheat-growing has been followed by mixed farming: the cultivation of mixed grains and root and fodder crops, combined with cattle rearing and dairying. This development of the eastern Prairies has been made necessary in part by the danger of continuing to use the soil for a single crop, in part by the need, created by the growing population and rising land values, to use the soil more intensively.

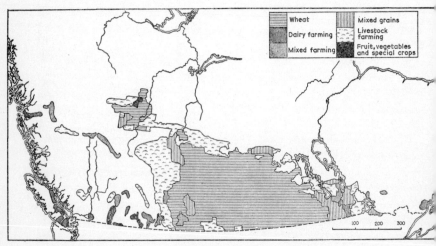

Wheat	Mixed grains
Dairy farming	Livestock farming
Mixed farming	Fruit, vegetables and special crops

Fig. 45. THE CANADIAN WEST: AGRICULTURAL REGIONS

The present agricultural pattern consists of an area of mixed farming in the east and a large curving belt of land given over largely to wheat growing; in its centre and also along its outer edge is cattle rearing.

The tendency for the western plains to be milder in climate than the area to the east has encouraged the spread of crop-farming outside the region of the grassy Prairies into the forests of the Peace River Valley. The Peace River, along with its chief tributary, the Smoky River, rises within the Rocky Mountains, but breaks through their main range and flows eastwards to join the great Mackenzie River system. Its valley is deepened considerably below the level of the third or highest Prairie step across which it flows. The lower altitudes, together with the less severe climate along the mountain edge, has encouraged the development of farming in the Peace River district. Wheat can be grown and is, in fact, a major crop. Other grains and fodder crops are raised, and cattle are reared. Some two million acres are occupied in this sub-arctic region, and the climate would probably permit a considerable extension of farmland.

The occupation of the Canadian Prairies by wheat farming has been permitted only by the development of quick maturing species, capable of ripening in the short summer. It was the "marquis" wheat, capable of maturing within 120 days, that permitted the agricultural development of the Prairie. This growing period has since been reduced to ninety days by the development of new wheats.

Winnipeg (233,617) is the oldest and largest city of the Prairie provinces. It is first and foremost a route centre, where the transcontinental railways converge to pass between Lake Winnipeg and the United States boundary. It has very large marshalling yards. Even its industries owe their existence here to the railways. The city gathers the agricultural products of a large part of the Prairie provinces and stores or processes them before sending them on to the east or the ocean ports. Wheat is the most important commodity handled. Much of it goes by rail to the twin Lake Superior ports of Fort William and Port Arthur; some goes direct to the ocean ports of Halifax, Montreal or Churchill, and it may be expected that with the completion of the St. Lawrence Seaway, direct shipments from the Great Lakes ports will increase at the expense of consignments sent by other routes.

Edmonton (113,116) and *Calgary* (100,044) play in the western Prairies a somewhat similar role to that of Winnipeg in the east. They are route centres in a developing agricultural region. This is indicated by their very rapid growth during the present century. Edmonton is especially important as the point of departure from one of the main transcontinental routes not only of the railways to the Peace River and Athabasca River but also of the highway to Yukon and Alaska. The industries of both cities are associated either with their role as railway centres or with the preparation of the agricultural products of the surrounding areas. Calgary is now the centre of the rapidly developing oil and natural gas field of Alberta.

Between Calgary and Edmonton in the west and Winnipeg in the east are several smaller towns: Regina (69,928), Saskatoon (52,732), Moose Jaw (24,336), Medicine Hat (12,859), all of them resembling in their functions the larger cities to the east and west of them.

THE ROCKY MOUNTAINS. The Cordilleran system, which in the United States had attained its greatest breadth of about 1,000 miles, narrows towards the north. In Montana its width is reduced to about

600 miles and at the Canadian border this is further diminished to 400 miles. The Pacific coast range is continued into Canada only as mountainous islands off the coast of British Columbia. The Cascade Range of Oregon and Washington becomes the Coast Range of Canada, and the intermontane plateaux are greatly reduced as the main range of the Rocky Mountains approaches the coastal mountains.

The Cordillera consists, in British Columbia, of three distinct belts of country lying roughly parallel to one another and to the Pacific coast. The Rocky Mountains in their restricted sense are part of the most easterly division. They are the highest mountains of the Canadian cordillera; they reach 12,972 feet in Mount Robson and there are several peaks above 11,000 feet. But the range is narrow, and its western side is straight and steep as it drops to the Rocky Mountain trench, one of the most conspicuous features of the whole system. It is a narrow valley with a level floor that can be followed in an almost straight line from within Montana in the south to Yukon in the north, a distance of over 1,000 miles. To the south it is occupied by the southward-flowing Kootenay River. An inconspicuous divide separates the Kootenay from the Columbia, here flowing northwards before it breaks westwards across the Selkirk Mountains. Then comes a tributary of the Columbia; then the Fraser; the Parsnip and the Finlay, which join to make the eastward flowing Peace River; then the Kechika and Hyland which form the Liard, another tributary of the Mackenzie.

West of the Rocky Mountain trench are mountains, lower than the Rockies themselves but geographically more complex. The Purcell, Selkirk and Nonashee Mountains occupy south-eastern British Columbia and continue into Montana, Idaho and Washington. They are shorter ranges lying obliquely to the Rocky Mountains, and their northern extremities are truncated by the Rocky Mountain trench. Other ranges border the trench on the west and continue into Yukon. They are crossed in northern British Columbia by the Alaska Highway, but are otherwise little known and almost unexplored.

These mountains comprise the most easterly of the three divisions of the cordillera. To the west of them is a belt of territory sometimes known as the Fraser and Nechako plateau. The term "plateau", however, rather underestimates the roughness of their surface. In part the plateau is a rolling upland, but generally the plateau nature of the region is apparent only in the conformity in height of the hill masses. The area has been deeply dissected by the Fraser and Okanogan Rivers and their tributaries.

The third region of the cordillera is the Coast Range, which continues the Cascades of Washington. Despite the presence of a few high peaks, including Mount Waddington (13,260 feet), the highest peak in British Columbia, the Coast Range is lower than the Rockies, and is furthermore broken into a number of segments by the rivers which rise in the plateau region and flow westwards across the Coast Range to the sea. Largest of these rivers is the Fraser, but the Skeena also opens up a broad valley route between the interior and the coast.

The coast of British Columbia is rugged in the extreme. The valleys which drop to the sea were further eroded during the Ice Age and their lower courses have since been drowned by a rise of sea level. Long fiords penetrate deeply into the mountains, and off-shore chains of islands continue the Coast Range of the United States. The largest of these is Vancouver Island, which is in reality a continuation of the Coast Range of Oregon and Washington. The Queen Charlotte Islands, further to the north-west, continue in the same direction.

CLIMATE AND SOIL. Mountains, it is said, make their own climate. The climate of the mountains of western Canada is as varied as might be expected in so diversified a region. The whole region lies in the path of the warm, humid westerlies. Near the coast the temperature range is small; winters are mild and summers cool. But beyond the coastal mountains the temperature range increases very sharply. In the Rockies the winters are long and severe. The summers are warm in the valleys, but their temperature is elsewhere greatly reduced by altitude. Rainfall is very heavy along the Coast Range, but the so-called plateaux of the interior are relatively dry—too dry in some parts for forest to grow. Rainfall again becomes heavy on the Rocky Mountains and its adjoining ranges, but the eastern foothills, lying in the rain-shadow, are very dry.

The soil types are adjusted to the climate. Over large parts of the mountains the land is virtually devoid of soil, but elsewhere it ranges from podsol in the rain-soaked Coast Range and parts of the Rocky Mountains to grey forest soils and even black chernozem in parts of the intermontane plateaux.

A rich forest covers the Coast Range, consisting largely of giant conifers, the Douglas fir, red cedar and spruce. This is one of the most valuable lumbering regions of Canada. But in the drier interior the trees are less developed, more scattered and in parts give way to long grass.

TRANSPORT AND COMMUNICATIONS. The mountains of British Columbia have never been a serious barrier to transport and communications. The main ranges are breached in many places, and across the plateaux the rivers have guided travellers as to-day they direct the course of the railways. The Rocky Mountains are crossed by rail at three points. Close to the United States border the Canadian Pacific Railroad between Medicine Hat and Vancouver crosses the Crow's Nest Pass at a height of 4,450 feet; 150 miles to the north-west is the Kicking Horse Pass at 5,339 feet, on the Canadian Pacific line from Calgary to Vancouver. The most northerly crossing is the Yellowhead Pass (3,711 feet) on the Canadian National line from Edmonton to Prince Rupert. A certain number of cross-routes follow the valleys and link the three main routes with one another within the mountain system. There is, however, little demand for transport within the plateau region. The forests here are too poor for lumbering to compete with that in the Coast Range, and agriculture is relatively undeveloped.

AGRICULTURE AND FORESTRY. Land fit for cultivation occurs in small patches along the valley floors. Its total extent is limited, and in very few places is the extensive, mechanized farming, such as is found in the Prairies, practicable. Farming in British Columbia is highly specialized. On the drier eastern side of Vancouver Island dairy farming is practised. Livestock and mixed farming occupy parts of the valley of the Fraser and of its tributaries. In the Okanogan Valley, one of the warmest and sunniest of the intermontane valleys, fruit-growing is important.

But agriculture is subsidiary both to lumbering and to mining. The lumber—mostly fir and cedar—is cut chiefly in the Coast Range. The logs are dragged to the river nearest the coast and rafted to the saw and pulp mills. The ease of water transport has encouraged the building of a few very large mills rather than a large number of smaller, such as are to be found around the margin of the Shield. Most of the large mills lie on Queen Charlotte Strait, the waterway between Vancouver Island and the mainland, or on the fiords that open from it.

MINERAL AND OTHER INDUSTRIES. Mining is, after forestry, the most important industry in British Columbia. Lead and zinc are mined in very large quantities in the Selkirk and Purcell Mountains, and a very large smelter is working at Trail, on the Columbia River, close to the United States border. Copper is also obtained in large quantities, much of it in association with gold, from mines in the Coast Range. The mines developed hitherto have been in the more populous and accessible regions. It is reasonable to expect that as surveying progresses in

the northern parts of British Columbia, further ore deposits, comparable
with those of the South, will be discovered.

Coal is mined on Vancouver Island, particularly in the Nanaimo
field on its eastern shore. There is also a small production from fields in
the Rocky Mountains, in the vicinity of the Crow's Nest Pass. The total
output of coal from the province does not amount to more than two
million tons a year.

Hydro-electric power offers a much larger potential source of power.
Only a small fraction of the power available has hitherto been developed:
industrial development has been too small to justify a larger production.
Most of the developed sources of power are either on the Columbia
River, where they supply electric current to the mines and smelters of
this area, or lie along the coast of Queen Charlotte Strait, where are
most of the saw and pulp mills.

Industries unconnected with the forests, the mines or the fisheries are
of no great importance. Food processing and preserving industries have
attained some slight importance, but the population of British Columbia is too small to justify the establishment of many consumers' goods
industries. It is cheaper to obtain such commodities from factories in
the East.

The Pacific coast of British Columbia is far less suited to the fishing
industry than the corresponding area of Europe. The continental shelf
is narrow, and the sea floor descends, within a few miles of the coast, to
the great depths of the ocean floor. This restricts not only the breeding
of the edible varieties of fish, but also the operation of a trawling industry. In spite of this, the British Columbian fisheries are large and
important, but they are given over mainly to salmon-fishing. In the
summer months the salmon, which have lived far from land in the
North Pacific, return to the freshwater rivers of the coast to lay their
eggs. It is during this "run" that the salmon are caught. A large part of
the salmon catch is canned, but refrigeration and fast rail transport
allow some to be sent to the market fresh. Halibut and other fish are
also caught in the deep-sea fisheries, which are operated from Prince
Rupert, New Westminster and other small ports.

POPULATION AND SETTLEMENT. The population of British Columbia is
only 1,165,210. *Vancouver*, the only large city in the province, has
557,725. It lies a short distance to the north of the mouth of the Fraser
River on the south shore of Burrard Inlet, which forms its harbour,
The city has grown fast; it is very largely a creation of the present century. It is the chief Pacific port of Canada; it has industries associated

with the lumber and fishing industries, as well as engineering and certain consumers' goods industries.

New Westminster (35,000) is a smaller port near the mouth of the Fraser River. The lumber and fishing industries are particularly important, but, as a major port, it has been supplanted by Vancouver, which is more favourably placed as the terminus of the Canadian Pacific Railroad.

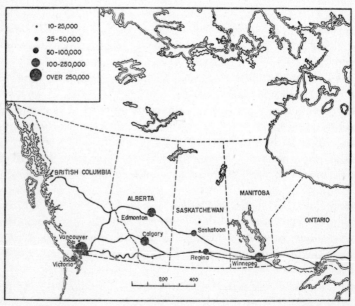

Fig. 46. THE CANADIAN WEST: CITIES AND TRANSPORT

Victoria (118,950), the capital of the province, lies at the southern extremity of Vancouver Island. As a port, Victoria has been superseded by Vancouver. It has those industries which are associated with the products of the region, but is primarily a governmental centre, engaged in the administration of the province. The other towns of British Columbia remain very small. Even Prince Rupert, terminus of the Canadian National Railroad, has only 9,200 inhabitants. Well-known mining and fruit-growing centres of the interior are even smaller.

There is a close similarity in physical environment, in climate and in products, between British Columbia and the neighbouring states of Washington, Oregon and Idaho. These are economically very much more developed than British Columbia. There is no reason in the environment itself why the latter should not develop as the former have done.

— 14 —

Canada: The North

THE North was defined arbitrarily in the previous chapter as the area lying north of the 60th parallel. This area is entirely one of of coniferous forest, tundra and ice-caps, but not all the area of tundra lies in these latitudes. It extends well to the south of 60° N., not only in the Rocky Mountains and Coast Range, but also around Hudson Bay and in northern Quebec. Alaska, which must be considered in this chapter, also extends at both its south-west and its south-east into much lower latitudes. The greater part of the region, however, is tundra, but into this tundra belt there intrudes a large area of forest. Forest is found along the south coast of Alaska; it occupies the valley of the Yukon River and of its major tributaries, and it lies along the Mackenzie Valley from Lake Athabasca almost to the Arctic Ocean.

CLIMATE AND VEGETATION. But to the east the coniferous forest is rare in these latitudes. Most of the area is tundra and in the far north-east are areas of ice-caps. The ice reaches its greatest extent and thickness in Greenland, where it covers all except a narrow periphery of this great island. There are also extensive ice-caps in Baffin Land, Ellesmere Land and the Parry Islands.

It might be said that, in general, the vegetation belts lie obliquely from north-west to south-east. The south-west of the Northland is forested, except where mountains are high enough to make this impossible. A belt stretching obliquely from northern Alaska to Labrador is made up of tundra, and the north-east is tundra with ice-caps on the higher ground. This implies a greater degree of mildness in the climate of the west than of the east. This is in keeping with the temperature of at least the northern half of the continent, and is to be attributed mainly to the moderating effect of the winds from the Pacific Ocean.

Almost the whole of the North has winters of exceptional severity.

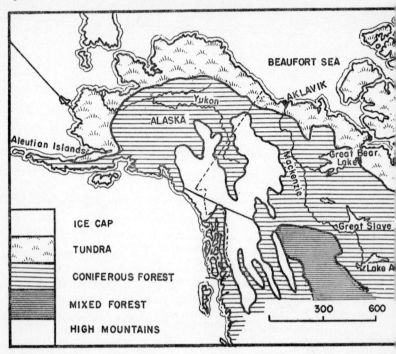

ICE CAP

TUNDRA

CONIFEROUS FOREST

MIXED FOREST

HIGH MOUNTAINS

Except on the coast of Alaska, at the southern tip of Greenland and in a few other relatively favoured spots, the January average is below zero: near the Arctic Ocean, more than 30 degrees below. On occasion temperatures drop to as low as 70 degrees below zero. The summers are short and cool. Only in the Mackenzie Valley is the July average likely to reach 60 degrees. Along the Arctic coast it may not even be 40 degrees. The growing season is short throughout the North. There may be in favoured areas, especially along the Mackenzie River, 75 or 80 days without frost; further north this may drop to 45 or less. To some extent the shortness of the growing season is offset by the great length of the summer days and the high amount of insolation. Nevertheless, agriculture is difficult and little practised. Grass grows well during the short summer, and hay can be made. Around the few settlements are meadows and dairy cattle; quick maturing vegetables are grown, but there is no possibility of the commercial production of crops.

For convenience of description the North is here divided into four parts: Alaska which is distinct politically if not geographically from the rest; the Canadian North-West, lying to the west of Hudson Bay; the Arctic archipelago, and lastly, Greenland.

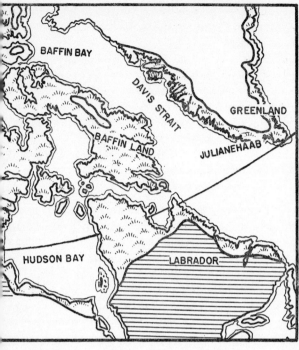

Fig. 47.
THE CANADIAN
NORTH, AND
ALASKA

ALASKA. The peninsula of Alaska is the most easily accessible part of the American North and extends westwards between the Arctic and Pacific Oceans; it reaches to within fifty miles of the coast of Russian Siberia and it sends two large fingers, the Aleutian Islands and the so-called "Panhandle", far into the temperate zone. Alaska has a latitudinal range of 20 degrees, and in area it is larger than either the Mid-West or the Old South.

The North American Cordillera makes a sharp bend in north-western Canada, and its constituent parts assume an approximately east-to-west direction. The same features are present as further to the south: the Pacific coast ranges, the interior plateau and the northern mountains which continue the line of the Mackenzie and Rocky Mountains. The coastal mountains are split by transverse valleys into a number of massive segments. In the south-east are the St. Elias Mountains, culminating in Mount Logan (19,850 feet). A branch from these mountains curves around Prince William Sound, forms the Kenai Peninsula and is continued, offshore, in Kodiak Island. Another branch, the Alaska Range, is curving further to the north, encloses Cook Inlet and the Matanuska Valley and runs out to sea in the long Alaskan peninsula continued in the Aleutian Islands. This range contains Mount McKinley (20,300 feet), the highest mountain in the continent, and also the active volcano, Mount Katmai.

North of the Alaska Range is a vast region of low plateau, interrupted by mountain ridges, and drained by the Kuskokwim and Yukon Rivers. This corresponds with the intermontane plateaux further to the south. Lastly, the Brooks Range shuts in the central plateau on its northern side. Its northern slopes sink to the coastal plain of the Arctic Ocean.

Alaska spans a wide climatic range. In the south it is only a little more severe than the coast of British Columbia, with cool winters and warm summers, but inland the climate deteriorates rapidly and January averages range from 10 to 30 degrees below zero.

Settlements. The earliest permanent white settlements were earlier here than in other parts of the American North. In 1784, a Russian trading station was set up on Kodiak Island, soon after the Russian occupation of eastern Siberia. In the following years a number of fur trading posts was established on the south and western coasts. The Russians pressed southwards into the Panhandle, where their activities were thought to present a threat to the interests of Great Britain and the United States. In 1867 Secretary of State Seward purchased Alaska from the Tsarist government of Russia for $7,200,000, a figure that seemed excessive at the time. The Russian settlers left, but their legacy remains in the place-names, in the occasional Russian style church, and in the sites of many of the permanent settlements.

In the meanwhile the earliest English-speaking settlers had moved in from Canada and had set up trading posts at Fort Yukon and in the Panhandle. After 1867, American settlements and population grew slowly for a generation, then, in the 1890's, increased sharply. Prospecting and mining and the development of the fisheries largely accounted for the expansion. There was after this little change in the population until the 1940's. Alaska suddenly found itself of great strategic importance and became a naval and military base of operations against the Japanese. The Alaska highway was built to improve the communications between central North America and Alaska. The total population rose from about 60,000 at the beginning of the century to about 128,643 in 1950. Of these over 90,000 were white.

The Economy of Alaska. Until recently agriculture had played a negligible role in the development of Alaska, but in 1935 an agricultural settlement was established in the Matanuska Valley, inland from Anchorage. In coastal Alaska the growing season is up to 140 days in the year, diminishing to 80 or 90 in the Yukon Valley. The soils are poor—podsols and grey forest soils—but they can be made to yield satisfactory crops with a heavy use of fertilizers. A little wheat is grown in the Matanuska Valley and other favoured areas in the south, but the chief crops are the hardy cereals, fodder crops and vegetables. In the Yukon Valley, agriculture faces greater difficulties. There the subsoil is likely to be permanently frozen, interfering with the natural drainage of the soil and making farming difficult. Although there are agricultural settlements near Fairbanks, it cannot be said that farming has a secure future in the interior and more northerly parts of Alaska.

Fishing, mining and forestry are the chief occupations of Alaska. As in British Columbia, the salmon is the most important fish caught, and its preparation for the market occupies very many canneries along the south coast. But other fish, including the halibut, the herring and the cod, are caught and exported. Related to the fisheries is the sealing industry. The Pribilof Islands, within the arc of the Aleutian Islands, is a breeding ground for the huge herd of North Pacific seal. The herd, which at one stage was brought near to extinction by indiscriminate hunting, has now been restored and its numbers are maintained by a careful regulation of sealing. The seals of the Pribilof Islands are the subject of *Seal Island* one of the series of nature films produced by Walt Disney.

Alaska has its share of the great mineral wealth of the Rocky Mountains. Mining activities have hitherto concentrated on minerals of high value in relation to their bulk, such as can be separated or concentrated under the exacting conditions of the North. Gold has been the most important mineral; it is produced mainly from alluvial deposits, or "placers". Gone are the days of the itinerant miner with his shovel and his pan. To-day, enormous dredgers work their way through the swamp, excavating the alluvial materials by means of buckets at the front, processing it in the middle, and discharging the waste in the rear. Other minerals—ores of copper, silver, mercury—have been located, but their exploitation has hitherto made little progress.

None of the settlements in Alaska is large. Fairbanks (5,625), on the Yukon River, is the largest inland centre of population. Anchorage (11,060) on the south coast; Kodiak on the island of the same name; Norne (1,852) on the west-facing coast, and Juneau (5,818), the capital of Alaska, Sitka, Petersburg, Wrangell and Ketchikan (5,203), all of them fishing centres in the Panhandle, together make up the urban settlements of Alaska. There are a few others, with only one or two hundred inhabitants, and a rather greater number of settlements

o

which in England would be termed hamlets. The growth and stability
of the population, which these settlements indicate, has prompted the
suggestion that Alaska, now a territory of the United States, might become the forty-ninth state of the Union. There are legitimate doubts
whether it is yet ripe for admission, but if the proposal is rejected it is
likely that political considerations in Washington, rather than the rate
of economic and political progress in Alaska, will be the determining
factors.

Alaska has in recent years developed a road network. The Alaska
highway comes in from Whitehorse in Yukon, and runs to Fairbanks,
with a number of branch roads to other centres of population. Fairbanks is joined to Anchorage and Valdez on the south coast. There are
a number of other short lengths of road, most of them linking a coast or
river station with an inland settlement. The only railway—the Alaskan
Railroad—runs from Seward on the south coast, through Anchorage, to
Fairbanks. Another short line, built during the period of the Yukon
gold rush, links Skagway in the Panhandle with Whitehorse in Yukon.

The recent economic development is based less on the intrinsic advantages and resources of the territory—though these are very much
greater than has commonly been supposed—than on the strategic importance of its location. It is the only part of American territory where
an enemy landing could be effected with little or no resistance. Such
an enemy force would find the penetration of the interior of the continent a matter of appalling difficulty. But in the fears of the moment
this saving factor is often forgotten. Alaska has become the politically
and militarily exposed frontier.

THE CANADIAN NORTH-WEST. This territory is limited by Alaska
to the west and Hudson Bay to the east, and on the north is the Arctic
Ocean. It spans the three major physical units which make up Canada:
the Shield, the central plains and the cordillera. The latter is represented by the triangular area to the south-west which comprises the
province of Yukon. The Coast Range of British Columbia is continued
in the St. Elias Range on the border of Yukon and Alaska. The Rocky
Mountains themselves are continued in the Selwyn Range, the Ogilire
and the Mackenzie Mountains. These pathless tangled mountains are
less high than the Rockies, but make up for this in their breadth and
complexity. Between these and the St. Elias Range is the basin of the
Yukon, in which are the few small settlements and the scanty mining
operations of Yukon.

The Mackenzie Valley is a northern extension of the prairies. Its

western margin is formed by the steep rise of the Mackenzie Mountains.
To the east, the younger rocks of the plains give place without conspicuous topographical feature to the older rocks of the Shield. The
junction of the two is, in fact, obscured by glacial deposits and the
spreading muskeg, or bog.

The Mackenzie River has developed along the outcrops of the
younger, softer beds of the prairies. The Great Slave Lake collects the
drainage of the Peace, Athabasca and other rivers, and discharges by
the Mackenzie. Half-way to the northern ocean it receives the drainage
of the Great Bear Lake. Between this point and Good Hope, the valley
is narrowed between the Mackenzie and the outlying Franklin Mountains. Below this the valley widens, and the river enters the ocean by a
vast and complex delta.

Settlement. This northern wilderness was first penetrated by white
men in the eighteenth century. They came in search of the fur-bearing
animals, whose skins they took and sent back to their trading bases on
Hudson Bay or the upper Great Lakes. They found here only a very
sparse Indian population scattered through the forests; along the coasts
were Eskimo communities, but few of the early trappers ever penetrated as far as this. Fur trapping remained the only commercial occupation. All the small permanent settlements were fur trading posts. It
was not until the later decades of the nineteenth century that the first
prospectors came. Alluvial gold was found in the Yukon Valley in 1896.
The movement of people into the area was only a degree less amazing
than that to California after the discovery of gold in 1848. Within a
few years the area became the politically separate Yukon Territory, and
Dawson City, amid the alluvial gold workings, was a rowdy, bustling
"boom" town.

In many parts this prosperity was short lived. Placer-deposits are
soon exhausted, and the population melted away from the little shack
towns. A third phase in the development of the North has come in the
past twenty years with a search for other metals than gold and the
establishment here of strategic routes and bases. Silver, lead and copper
—none of them normally found in placer deposits—are being worked.
Oil is being drilled along the Mackenzie Valley in quantities at least
sufficient for local needs, and the discovery of radium on the eastern
shore of the Great Bear Lake in the old rocks of the Shield has led to a
feverish activity by prospectors and miners.

Associated with these recent developments is the construction of a
hard surfaced road from Edmonton, Alberta, through the Peace River

Valley, across the main range of the Rockies by the Liard Valley, and so into Yukon. The purpose of the road was largely strategic, but it has greatly diminished the difficulty of transporting supplies to these remote mining centres and will certainly hasten the development of resources along its route.

But the Alaska Highway only just touches the Canadian North. A rough road follows the Mackenzie River as far as the oil-field of Norman Wells. The river itself is the main highway during the short open season. But the whole of the eastern part of this area is a pathless wilderness.

The permanent settlements of the North West have become quite numerous, but all are small. In general a few wooden houses are gathered round a mission and a store. The population is likely to be made up of a few white traders, prospectors and miners, perhaps a doctor and a priest, and a small group of Indians and half-breeds.

THE ARCTIC ISLANDS. North of the shores of the continent is a group of islands, large and small, most of them unexplored, all of them little known and almost uninhabited. They represent a northward extension of the Shield, here partially submerged to form the maze of islands. Most of them are no higher and not more rugged than the Shield itself, but in the far north, in Ellesmere Land, Devon Island and the Sverdrup Islands, the surface is more mountainous than any part of the Shield itself.

There is a presumption that the islands, being similar in geological structure and age to the Shield, are as highly mineralized. But the problems of development may well seem insuperable. Summer is limited to a few weeks when the temperature may hover around the forties. In winter, up to 100 degrees of frost are far from uncommon. For two-thirds or even three-quarters of the year the average monthly temperature is below freezing. The channels between the islands are almost continually ice-covered. In summer the pack ice retreats from the coast of the continent, but even in July the ice-glint can be seen in the northern sky from Aklavik at the Mackenzie River delta. The North West Passage from the Atlantic to the Pacific Oceans is an illusion. The channel is there, as the sixteenth-century voyagers suspected, and a swift ship, equipped for Arctic exploration, may sail through in the short open summer, but the route has no commercial significance and is closed to the humble freighter. Even the Hudson Strait, between Baffin Island and the northern shores of Quebec, is only open for some three months, too short a period for the development of a vigorous commerce with the ports of Hudson Bay.

There are no permanent settlements in the Arctic Islands. The only regular inhabitants are the Eskimo, who form a number of small, semi-nomadic colonies on the shores of Victoria Island, Southampton Island and Baffin Land, and on the shores of the mainland opposite. They live mainly on fish and seal meat, supplemented in recent years by purchases from the traders and gifts from missionaries.

There are virtually no trees; driftwood supplies the needs of the Eskimo. The land surface is covered for most of the year under snow. In the short summer this melts away to reveal either bare rock or a barren waste of mosses, lichens and muskeg.

GREENLAND. The island of Greenland is distinguished from the rest of the Arctic Islands not only by virtue of its size and its almost complete covering of ice, but also by its political allegiance. It is part of the Kingdom of Denmark. Discovered by the Norsemen in the tenth century and settled by them, it remained in close touch with Iceland and North-western Europe until the later Middle Ages. Then, at the very time that European interest was being awakened in transatlantic and distant voyages, the contact between Greenland and Iceland lapsed. The small European settlement of southern Greenland died out in the late medieval conditions of worsening climate.

Greenland is composed of rocks similar to those of Labrador and Baffin Land. The initially mountainous area has been depressed under the great weight of accumulated ice. The height of the Greenland ice-cap is over 9,000 feet above sea level; its thickness is as much as 10,000 feet.

The ice-sheet is lens-shaped in section. It thins towards the margin, and the underlying rock here comes to the surface and gives rise to a coastline of exceptional ruggedness. Glaciers, moving down to the coast from the ice-cap, have carved long fiords. In spring and summer the glaciers "calve", sending icebergs out into the south-moving current of Davis and Denmark Straits. The icebergs slowly melt as they reach lower latitudes, but not before they create a very considerable hazard to navigation.

In southern Greenland there is a belt of land, up to 120 miles wide, between the permanent margin of the ice and the coast. This narrows towards the north, and, at a latitude of about 75 degrees, the ice-sheet extends into the sea, blanketing completely the underlying rock. In the extreme north, however, the ice is less extensive, owing to the reduced precipitation of high arctic regions, and here the area of exposed rock is larger.

The climate of Greenland requires no comment. It is cold throughout the year. Around the coast the snow melts away during the short summer, and the mosses provide grazing for reindeer. Here colonies of Eskimo live, like those of the Canadian North, by fishing and tending the half-wild animals of the tundra. The only industries are extractive. Greenland is the only significant producer of the mineral cryolite, used in the electrolytic refining of aluminium. This is mined at Ivigtut, on Arsukfiord on the south-west coast. Marble is mined and exported from Marmorlite. There is even a very small production of coal. The fisheries are of vital importance for the inhabitants of Greenland, and there is a small export of canned and preserved fish. But there is no future in the economic resources of Greenland, and financially it is a liability rather than an asset to the Danish crown. Its importance is strategic. In 1941, by agreement between the United States and Danish governments, Greenland was placed under the protection of the former. This step was not taken for the sake of the few inhabitants of Greenland, but rather to allow the United States to watch more effectively this island which lies so close to her own front door.

American control continues with, as its object, the protection of the approaches to the North American continent. An air base is maintained at Thule, in far north-western Greenland, from which it may be possible to protect the transpolar approaches to the continent.

— 15 —

The Continent in Perspective

T HE English traveller to America finds many things that are unfamiliar and some to which he finds it hard to accustom himself. He has to learn a new language, made all the more difficult for him by its deceptive similarity to his own. There are tricks of spelling and pronunciation which he may acquire, but the idiosyncrasies of meaning and the differences in the overtones of words constantly bewilder him. The American walks (when he does walk) on the "sidewalk" but drives his car on the "pavement". An Englishman aroused consternation in his hostess when at dinner he commended her upon the excellence of her "joint". But such trifles generally cause only amusement; there are deeper differences between English and American culture.

Along with the differences in language there go differences in social practices and customs. The contrasts are sufficiently great for the visitor to be always on his guard. He must accustom himself to a different speed of life. America is a land where machines move fast—very much faster than in Europe—but where people move very much more slowly. This he will have realized from his encounter with the American immigration and customs officials. Beneath the superficial bustle and hurry —the taxis on Broadway, the transcontinental trains and the fast moving production line—the pace of life is leisurely and even slow. The American is always ready to stand and talk.

Our traveller will detect in American life many traits that derive from the frontier days. The Americans are, as a whole, generous and hospitable and lacking in reserve and inhibitions. Their country is cast in a larger mould than Europe. Distances are greater; the hazards of storm, tempest and flood are bigger and more immediate than in Europe. In such circumstances the feeling of fellowship and mutual dependence between people is stronger. The eighteenth-century farmer from Martha's Vineyard showed himself, in the passage quoted at the beginning of this book, to be aware of this sense of comradeship and equality, greater than that which he had known in Europe.

These excellent qualities are deep rooted in the American past; so also is a vague distrust of other nations and other continents. Long cut off from direct contact with different peoples and places, the homespun American farmer has come to suspect the outsider, always fearing that he may be outwitted by the cleverer foreigner either in business or in politics. At intervals in Americans' relations with other countries there comes a revulsion of feeling, a sense that they have gone too far, have shown their hand too openly, and will be outwitted and victimized by the foreigner, just as they themselves outwitted and defeated the Indian and the Mexican. They pull back and hold themselves aloof until political or economic necessity convinces them that they cannot go on like this and obliges them to make fresh approaches to other nations. This attitude, so crudely and incorrectly termed "isolationist", may be weakening to-day, but it will remain until all sections of American opinion are at last convinced that the future of their country is irretrievably and inextricably bound up with that of all their neighbours. This conviction is very far indeed from being general.

In many respects Canada is in an intermediate position between Great Britain and the United States. This is very apparent. The American accent is less strong; English shops have branches in Canadian cities; the Queen's portrait appears on the postage stamps, and letters are posted in metal containers of pillar-box red. But the American way of life is strongly marked: the outward speed and bustle, the large scale of industrial undertakings, the commercialism and the vulgarity.

In a more important way, also, Canada occupies an intermediate position. Canada is a member of the Commonwealth, sharing a common sovereign with Great Britain and some other parts of the Commonwealth. This legal and sentimental tie binds Canada closely with nations outside the American continent. The policy of the United States has clearly to envisage the defence of Canada and joint military plans are prepared and manœuvres organized for the defence of the two nations. On the other hand, the military commitments of Canada are closely bound up with those of Great Britain, the Dominions and the dependent territories. In what ways Canada has, in recent years, helped to bridge the diplomatic and political gaps that have on occasion shown themselves between Great Britain and the United States we shall not know for a long time. But in a subtle way this double role of Canada serves to take the edge from the isolationist trends in American policy and public opinion. The United States views Canada in a light very different from that in which she regards her other neighbour, Mexico. The undefended "boundary" between Canada and the United States is often a matter for self-congratulation for both parties. But towards Mexico the United States have only a "border", with its connotations of lawlessness. This condition fortunately no longer prevails, but the folk-memory is here one of violence rather than of peaceful co-operation.

Canada is, to outward appearances, a poorer country than the United States. National income per head of population, and standards of living, are somewhat lower in Canada than in the United States. In this respect, too, Canada occupies an intermediate position between the latter and England. Until recently the Canadian dollar was worth in the money market a few cents less than the American. It is now worth a cent or two more. This change reflects a change in the relative economic positions of the two. In the past Canada occupied, in the minds of many Americans, something of a "colonial" status. It was a "poor sister", with little by way of industrial development and resources that could compare with those of the United States.

This has changed. The period of the Second World War saw a sharp development of manufacturing industries in Canada, stimulated by governmental agencies and contracts. Natural resources proved larger than at first seemed likely, and investment—much of it American—in their exploitation is bringing about a "boom" not unlike that in the United States in the late nineteenth century. The mining or extraction of iron ore, petroleum, natural gas and uranium are merely the most conspicuous of many rapidly expanding industries. Hydro-electric power, the exploitation of other non-ferrous metals, lumbering, paper and pulp, the smelting industries and the automobile and consumer goods industries are all growing in importance. Canada's declared intention of going ahead with the St. Lawrence Seaway project, with or without American co-operation, is symptomatic of the shift in the relationship of the two countries.

One may ask whether a reversal of the relative positions of Canada and the United States is possible or likely. Much of the capital now being invested in Canada comes from the United States, but an equipment is now being accumulated which will allow Canada in the not-too-distant future to generate capital herself on a very considerable scale. One may anticipate a period in which economic growth in Canada will be faster than that in the United States, but that Canada could overtake the United States does not appear within the limits of possibility. About 16 per cent of the population of the United States is engaged in agriculture. There is no chance of a farming population of anything near this size gaining a living from the soil of Canada. And a smaller farming population is likely to restrict the growth of those other industries for which the farmer provides a market.

The expansion of population and both extractive and manufacturing industries, which in the past decades has characterized Canada and the United States alike, is likely to continue for at least the near future. And with them will grow the economic and political power of both countries.

The overwhelming strength of the United States is to-day a common-place. She has at various times in recent years subsidized the economy of most western European countries, and the post-war recovery of those that had suffered heavily during the war would have been greatly delayed without powerful and generous American assistance. Great Britain has been heavily dependent on the United States, and if at the present time she is showing a degree of economic independence, this happier position itself derives from earlier American help.

The concentration in the North American continent of so much economic, and along with it, political power must necessarily arouse fears and anxieties in less favoured nations. Much of the world watches the American stock-market in the knowledge that a recession in Wall Street is likely to have serious consequences in every other capitalist country. In other quarters apprehension is expressed that so much power should be backed with so little political maturity and experience. It is true that both the United States and Canada have been active and prominent participants in world affairs for only a short time. But leader-ship is a sobering experience, and it would be false to underestimate either the political capacity or the sagacity of these young nations. Americans play the game of politics differently from Europeans. The latter must not be deceived by the froth that rises to the surface of the American political scene. Beneath is much wisdom, thought and careful planning. The role of world leadership is not lightly assumed nor thoughtlessly borne, and in America the body of opinion that favours the gradual strengthening of the bonds between the members of the "North Atlantic Triangle" is large and growing. The best contribution that each can make to this end lies in a better understanding of the geography and history, the problems and policies of the other two.

Bibliography[1]

Abbreviations Used

A.A.A.G.   *Annals of the Association of American Geographers*, Lancaster, Pennsylvania.

A.A.A.P.S.S. Annals of the American Association of Political and Social Science, Philadelphia

Econ. Geog. *Economic Geography*, Clark University, Massachusetts.

Geog.   *Geography*, The Geographical Association, Sheffield.

G.J.   *Geographical Journal*, Royal Geographical Society, London.

G.R.   *Geographical Review*, American Geographical Society, New York.

H.M.S.O.   Her Majesty's Stationery Office.

Texts and General Books

J. R. SMITH and M. O. PHILLIPS, *North America*, Harcourt Brace, 1942.

C. L. WHITE and E. J. FOSCUE, *North America*, Prentice Hall, 1950.

L. RODWELL JONES and P. W. BRYAN, *North America*, Methuen, 1950.

GRIFFITH TAYLOR, *Canada*, Methuen, 1947.

Canada Yearbook. Published annually by the Canadian Government Bureau of Statistics.

A. W. CURRIE, *Economic Geography of Canada*, Macmillan, 1945.

J. D. GIBSON, *Canada's Economy in a Changing World*, Canadian Institute of International Affairs, 1948.

H. H. McCARTY, *The Geographic Basis of American Economic Life*, Harper, 1940.

A. J. WRIGHT, *United States and Canada*, Appleton-Century, 1948.

C. C. TAYLOR and OTHERS, *Rural Life in the United States*, Knopf, 1949.

A. G. MEZERIK, *The Revolt of the South and West*, Duell, 1946.

[1] See p. 222, *Note on Availability of Books.*

G. J. MILLER, A. E. PARKINS and B. HUDGINS, *North America*, Wiley, 1954.

Statistical Abstract of the United States, U.S. Bureau of the Census, published annually.

Agricultural Statistics, U.S. Department of Agriculture, published annually.

Annual Report on the Mineral Production of Canada, Canadian Bureau of Statistics, published annually.

Minerals Yearbook, U.S. Department of the Interior, published annually.

1. Discovery and Exploration

J. B. BREBNER, *Discoverers and Explorers of North America*, Black, 1933.

F. A. KIRKPATRICK, *Spanish Conquistadores*, Black, 1934.

J. F. RIPPY, *Historic Evolution of Hispanic America*, Crofts, 1947.

C. E. CARRINGTON, *The British Overseas*, Cambridge, 1950.

E. C. KIRKLAND, *History of American Economic Life*, Crofts, 1939.

M. NEWBIGIN, *Canada, The Great River, the Lands and the Men*, Christophers, 1926.

R. H. BROWN, *Historical Geography of the United States*, Harcourt Brace, 1948.

R. H. BROWN, *Mirror for Americans*, American Geological Society, 1943.

E. W. GILBERT, *Exploration of Western America*, Cambridge, 1933.

R. A. BILLINGTON, *Westward Expansion*, Macmillan (N.Y.), 1949.

B. DE VOTO, *The Course of Empire*, Houghton Mifflin, 1952.

F. PARKMAN, *The Oregon Trail*, Penguin Books, 1949

J. T. ADAMS, *Epic of America*, G. Routledge, 1938.

S. E. MORISON and H. S. COMMAGER, *The Growth of the American Republic*, Vol. 1, Oxford, 1943.

2. Relief, Climate, Soil and Vegetation

N. M. FENNEMAN, *Physiography of Eastern America*, McGraw Hill, 1938.

N. N. FENNEMAN, *Physiography of Western America*, McGraw Hill, 1931.

W. W. ATWOOD, *Physiographic Provinces of North America*, Ginn, 1940.

R. F. FLINT, *Glacial Geology and the Pleistocene Epoch*, Chaps. 11-14, Wiley, 1947.

R. F. FLINT and OTHERS, *Glacial Map of North America*, Geological Society of America, Special Papers 60, 1945.

"Soils and Men", *U.S. Yearbook of Agriculture 1938*, U.S. Department of Agriculture.

"Climate and Man", *U.S. Yearbook of Agriculture 1941*, U.S. Department of Agriculture.

E. A. ACKERMAN, "The Koeppen Classification of Climates in North America", *G.R.*, Vol. 31, 1941, 105–11.

S. S. VISHER, *Climatic Atlas of the United States*, Harvard University Press, Mass., 1954.

S. N. FLORA, *Tornadoes of the United States*, Oklahoma, 1954.

R. DE C. WARD, "Rainfall Types in the United States", *G.R.*, Vol. 31, 1917, 131–44.

S. S. VISHER, "Droughts and Floods in the United States", *Econ. Geog.*, Vol. 19, 1943, 1–15.

R. J. RUSSELL, "Dry Climates of the United States", *University of California Publications in Geography*, Vol. 5, 1931–2, Nos. 1 and 5.

GEORGE H. T. KIMBLE, *Our American Weather*, McGraw-Hill, 1955.

"TREES", *U.S. Yearbook of Agriculture, 1949.*

"GRASS", *U.S. Yearbook of Agriculture, 1948.*

"Science in Farming", *U.S. Yearbook of Agriculture, 1943–1947.*

"Crops in Peace and War", *U.S. Yearbook of Agriculture, 1950–1951.*

"Plant Diseases", *U.S. Yearbook of Agriculture, 1953.*

3. Land, Minerals, Population, Transport

L. I. DUBLIN (ed.), "The American People", *A.A.A.P.S.S.*, Vol. 188, 1936.

P. K. WHELPTON, "A History of Population Growth in the United States", *Scientific Monthly*, Vol. 67, 1948, 277–88.

F. J. BROWN and J. S. ROUCEK (ed.), *Our Racial and National Minorities*, Prentice Hall, 1937.

J. R. WHITACKER and E. A. ACKERMAN, *American Resources*, Harcourt Brace, 1951.

J. J. PARSONS. "The Geography of Natural Gas in the United States," *Econ. Geog.*, Vol. 26, 1950, 162–78.

J. E. COLLIER, "Aluminum Resources of the United States", *Econ. Geog.*, Vol. 24, 1948, 74–7.

O. E. BAKER, "Agricultural Regions of North America", *Econ. Geog.*, various references, Vols. 2–9, 1926–33.

"Marketing", *U.S. Yearbook of Agriculture, 1954*, Government Printing Office.

G. E. McLAUGHLIN, *Growth of American Manufacturing Areas*, Part II, Pittsburgh, 1938.

J. E. ALEXANDER, "Industrial Expansion in the United States", *Econ. Geog.*, Vol. 28, 1952, 128–42.

E. L. ULLMAN, "The Railroad Pattern of the United States", *G.R.*, Vol. 39, 1949, 242–56.

Productivity Team Report on Iron and Steel, H.M.S.O., 1952.

M. JEFFERSON, "The Great Cities of the United States, 1940", *G.R.*, Vol. 31, 1941, 479–87.

Land Utilization, 1950, U.S. Departments of Commerce and Agriculture, Government Printing Office.

C. F. KOHN, "Population Trends in the U.S. since 1940", *G.R.*, Vol. 35, 1945, 98–106.

W. E. PRATT and D. GOOD, *World Geography of Petroleum*, American Geographical Society, 1950.

R. HARTSHORNE, "A New Map of the Dairy Areas of the United States", *Econ. Geog.*, Vol. 11, 1935, 347–55.

M. CLAWSON, *The Western Range Livestock Industry*, McGraw Hill, 1950.

E. B. ALDERFER and H. E. MICHL, *Economics of American Industry*, McGraw Hill, 1950.

J. B. WALKER, *The Epic of American Industry*, Harper, 1949.

R. HARTSHORNE, "A New Map of the Manufacturing Belt of North America", *Econ. Geog.*, Vol. 13, 1937, 45–53.

A. J. WRIGHT, "Recent Changes in the Concentration of Manufacturing", *A.A.A.G.*, Vol. 55, 1945, 144–66.

4. New York

NEW YORK CITY, *Fortune*, Vol. 20, No. 1, 1939.

J. K. WRIGHT, "The Diversity of New York City", *G.R.*, Vol. 26, 1936, 620–39.

A. NEVINS and J. A. KROUT, *The Greater City: New York, 1898–1948*, Columbia, 1948.

A. G. OGILVIE, "New York and its Region", *Geog.*, Vol. 15, 1929, 199–214.

H. H. McCARTY, *The Geographical Basis of American Economic Life*, Harper, 1940, Chap. 25, Metropolitan New York.

NEW YORK CITY, *Focus*, Vol. 2, No. 10, 1952, American Geographical Society.

NEW YORK PANORAMA, *Federal Writers' Project*, Random House, 1938.

F. WHITBECK, "New York State Barge Canal: Expectations and Realisations", *Econ. Geog.*, Vol. 4, 1928, 196–206.

5. New England

J. K. WRIGHT (ed.), *New England's Prospect*, American Geographical
Society, 1933.
J. D. BLACK, *The Rural Economy of New England*, Harvard, 1950.
S. E. HARRIS, *The Economics of New England*, Harvard, 1952.
H. F. WILSON, *The Hill Country of New England, Its Social and Economic
History*, 1936.
C. D. HYSON and A. NEAL, "New England's Economic Prospects",
Harvard Business Review, Vol. 26, 1948, 156–180.
S. A. ANDERSON and F. M. WOODWARD, "Agricultural Vermont",
Econ. Geog., Vol. 8, 1932, 12–42.
E. M. WILSON, "The Aroostook Valley", *G.R.*, Vol. 16, 1926, 196–205.
W. ISARD and J. H. CUMBERLAND, "New England as a Possible Location
for an Integrated Iron and Steel Works", *Econ. Geog.*, Vol. 26, 1950,
245–59.

6. Middle Atlantic States

R. E. and M. MURPHY, *Pennsylvania, a Regional Geography*, Pennsylvania
Book Service, 1937.
L. E. KLIMM and OTHERS, *Philadelphia: Its Site and Situation*, Bull.
Geographical Society, Philadelphia, Vol. 33, 1935, 1–27.
P. BLOOD, "Factors in the Economic Development of Baltimore, Mary-
land", *Econ. Geog.*, Vol. 13, 1937, 186–208.
L. WHITE and E. J. FOSCUE, "The Iron and Steel Industry of Sparrows
Point, Md.", *G.R.*, Vol. 21, 1931, 244–58.

7. Appalachians

R. E. and M. MURPHY, "Anthracite Region of Pennsylvania", *Econ.
Geog.*, Vol. 14, 1938, 338–48.
L. WHITE, "The Iron and Steel Industry of Birmingham, Ala. District",
Econ. Geog., Vol. 8, 1932, 349–65.
L. WHITE, "The Iron and Steel Industry of the Pittsburgh District",
Econ. Geog., Vol. 4, 1928, 115–39.
R. E. MURPHY and H. E. SPITTAL, "Movements in the Center of Coal
Mining in the Appalachian Plateaus", *G.R.*, Vol. 35, 1945, 624–33.
R. E. MURPHY and H. E. SPITTAL, "A New Production Map of the
Appalachian Bituminous Coal Region", *A.A.A.G.*, Vol. 34, 1944,
164–72.

R. HARTSHORNE, "Location Factors in the Iron and Steel Industry", *Econ. Geog.*, Vol. 4, 1928, 241–52.

J. L. RICH, "A Bird's Eye Cross Section of the Central Appalachian Mountains and Plateau". *G.R.*, Vol. 29, 1939, 338–48.

H. F. RAUP, "The Susquehanna Corridor, a neglected trans-Appalachian route", *G.R.*, Vol. 30, 1940, 439–50.

C. M. ZEIRER, "Scranton's Industrial Integrity", *Econ. Geog.*, Vol. 8, 1932, 70–86.

R. E. MURPHY, "Johnstown and York; a comparative study of two industrial cities", *A.A.A.G.*, Vol. 25, 1935, 175–96.

8. Mid-West

L. DURAND, JNR., "The American Dairy Region", *Econ. Geog.*, Vol. 23, 1947, 32–40.

E. W. MILLER, "Cleveland: A Great Lakes Port", *Scientific Monthly*, Vol. 59, 1944, 197–204.

D. R. BERGSMARK, "Minneapolis, the Mill City", *Econ. Geog.*, Vol. 3, 1927, 391–7.

H. M. MAYER, "The Railway Terminal Problem of Central Chicago", *Econ. Geog.*, Vol. 21, 1945, 62–76.

R. H. WHITBECK, "Economic Aspects of the Glaciation of Wisconsin", *A.A.A.G.*, Vol. 3, 1913, 62–87.

H. L. SMITH, "Agricultural Land Use in Iowa", *Econ. Geog.*, Vol. 25, 1949, 190–200.

W. G. LEZIUS, "The Lake Port at Toledo", *Econ. Geog.*, Vol. 12, 1936, 197–204.

J. K. ROSE, "Corn Field and Climate in the Corn Belt", *G.R.*, Vol. 26, 1936.

E. SHAW, "Swine Production in the Corn Belt of the U.S.", *Econ. Geog.*, Vol. 12, 1936, 359–72.

W. E. McINTYRE, "Land Utilisation of Three Typical Upland Prairie Townships", *Econ. Geog.*, Vol. 25, 1949, 260–74.

H. L. SMITH, "Agricultural Land Use in Iowa", *Econ. Geog.*, Vol. 25, 1949, 190–200.

C. M. DAVIS, "The Cities and Towns of the High Plains of Michigan", *G.R.*, Vol. 28, 1938, 664–73.

R. HARTSHORNE, "The Twin City District", *G.R.*, Vol. 22, 1932, 431–42.

B. HUDGINS, "The Evolution of Metropolitan Detroit", *Econ. Geog.*, Vol. 21, 1945, 206–20.

J. W. ALEXANDER, "Manufacturing in the Rock River Valley", *A.A.A.G.*, Vol. 40, 1950, 237–53.

A. D. CUTSHALL, "Industrial Geography of the Lower Wabash Valley", *Econ. Geog.*, Vol. 17, 1944, 297–307.

R. R. RAWSON, "The Agricultural Geography of the Dakotas", *Geog.*, 25, 1940, 6–17.

P. W. BRYAN, *Man's Adaptation of Nature*, London, 1933, Chapters on the Corn Belt and Chicago.

9. The South

Report on the Economic Conditions in the South, National Emergency Council, Government Printing Office, 1938.

J. J. PARSONS, "Recent Industrial Development in the Gulf South", *G.R.*, Vol. 40, 1950, 67–83.

A. DAVIS and OTHERS, *Deep South*, Cambridge, Mass., 1941.

L. C. COPELAND and W. K. MCPHERSON, "Industrial Trends in the Tennessee Valley", *Social Forces*, Vol. 24, 1946, 273–83.

Tennessee Valley Resources, T.V.A., 1947.

J. HUXLEY, T.V.A., *An Adventure in Planning*, Architectural Press, 1941.

D. LILLIENTHAL, T.V.A., *Democracy on the March*, Penguin Books, 1944.

R. M. BROWN, "Cotton Manufacturing: North and South", *Econ. Geog.*, Vol. 4, 1928, 74–88.

J. BYNUM, "Piedmont North Caroline and Textile Production", *Econ. Geog.*, Vol. 4, 1928, 232–40.

G. E. MCLAUGHLIN and S. ROBOCR, *Why Industry Moves South*, National Planning Association, Washington, 1949.

C. B. HOOVER and B. U. RATCHFORD, *Economic Resources and Policies of the South*, Macmillan (N.Y.), 1951.

A. E. PARKINS, *The South: its Economic-Geographic Development*, Chapman and Hall, 1938.

R. B. VANCE, *All These People: The Nation's Human Resources in the South*, North Carolina, 1945.

W. ZELINSKY, "The Changing South", *Focus*, Vol. II, No. 2, 1951.

C. O. SAUER, *The Geography of the Ozark Highlands*, Chicago, 1920.

F. G. MORRIS, "Soil Erosion in the S.E. United States", *G.J.*, Vol. 90, 1937, 363–70.

W. ARNELL, "French Survivals in the Mississippi Valley", *Geog.*, Vol. 27, 1942, 89–94.

I. BOWMAN, *Forest Physiography*, Wiley, 1914.

P

P. R. Crowe, "Rainfall Regions in S.E. United States", *London Essays in Geography*, Longmans, 1951.

R. B. Vance, *Human Factors in Cotton Culture*, University of North Carolina, 1929.

H. Hatcher, "Dairying in the South", *Econ. Geog.*, Vol. 20, 1944, 54–64.

M. Prunty, Junr., "Land Occupance in the South-East: Landmarks and Forecast", *G.R.*, Vol. 42, 1952, 439–61.

C. F. Kohn, "Development of Dairy Farming in Mississippi", *Econ. Geog.*, Vol. 19, 1943, 188–95.

L. C. Post, "The Rice Country of South-West Louisiana", *G.R.*, Vol. 30, 1940, 574–90.

L. L. Stephen, "Vegetable Production in the Northern Everglades", *Econ. Geog.*, Vol. 20, 1944, 79–101.

S. N. Dicken, "Central Florida Farm Landscape", *Econ. Geog.*, Vol. 11, 1935, 85–103.

P. Selznick, *T.V.A. and the Grass Roots*, California, 1949.

R. B. Vance, *Human Geography of the South*, University of North Carolina, 1932.

10. Great Plains

W. Calef, "Winter of 1948–9 in the Great Plains", *A.A.A.G.*, Vol. 40, 1950, 267–92.

H. L. Shantz, "Natural Vegetation of the Great Plains Region", *A.A.A.G.*, Vol. 13, 1923, 81–107.

C. F. Marbut, "Soils of the Great Plains", *A.A.A.G.*, Vol. 13, 1923, 41–66.

O. E. Baker, "Agriculture of the Great Plains", *A.A.A.G.*, Vol. 13, 1923, 110–67.

L. Olson, "Migration and Economic Opportunity in the Great Plains", *G.R.*, Vol. 26, 1936, 670–2.

The Missouri Basin: Development Programme, U.S. Government Printing Office, 1952.

"Soils and Men", *U.S. Yearbook of Agriculture, 1938*, Government Printing Office.

W. P. Webb, *The Great Plains*, Ginn & Co., 1931.

R. E. Ward, "The Northern Great Plains as Producer of Wheat", *Econ. Geog.*, Vol. 22, 1946, 231–44.

E. Mather, "The Production and Marketing of Wyoming Beef Cattle", *Econ. Geog.*, Vol. 26, 1950, 81–93.

The Missouri River Basin Development Program, The Missouri Inter Agency Committee, 1952.

J. R. BORCHERT, "The Climate of the Central North American Grassland", *A.A.A.G.*, Vol. 40, 1950, 1–39.

J. S. GIBSON, "Agriculture of the Southern High Plains", *Econ. Geog.*, Vol. 8, 1932, 245–61.

W. G. V. BALCHIN and N. PYE, "Recent Economic Trends in Arizona", *G.J.*, Vol. CXX, 1954, 156–73.

H. J. WOOD, "Some Aspects of Irrigation Development in the Western United States", *Geog.*, 21, 1936, 201–15.

11. The West

R. M. GLENDENNING, "Desert Change: A Study in the Boulder Dam Area", *Scientific Monthly*, Vol. 61, 1945, 181–93.

C. B. HUTCHINSON (ed.), *California Agriculture*, California, 1946.

E. EISELEN, "The Central Valley Project, 1947", *Econ. Geog.*, Vol. 23, 1947, 22–31.

J. J. PARSONS, "California Manufacturing", *G.R.*, Vol. 39, 1949, 229–41.

E. L. ULLMAN, "Rivers as Regional Bonds: The Colombia-Snake Example", *G.R.*, Vol. 41, 1954, 210–25.

S. M. WOLLE, *The Bonanza Trail*, Indiana University, 1954.

W. P. MORRELL, *The Gold Rushes*, Black, 1940.

C. D. FORDE, *Habitat, Economy and Society*, Methuen, 1945, Chap. XII, "The Hopi and Yuma".

G. B. BARBOUR, "Boulder Dam and its Geographical Setting", *G.J.*, Vol. 86, 1935, 498–504.

G. B. BARBOUR, "Harnessing the Colombia River", *G.J.*, Vol. 96, 1940, 233–42.

"Soil and Water Conservation in the Pacific North-West", *Farmers' Bulletin*, No. 1773, U.S. Department of Agriculture, 1937.

M. H. SAUNDERSON, *Western Land and Water Use*, Oklahoma, 1950.

N. MIRKOWICH, "Recent Trends in Population Distribution in California", *G.R.*, Vol. 39, 1949, 229–41.

H. LEMONS and R. D. TONSLEY, "The Washington Apple Industry", *Econ. Geog.*, Vol. 21, 1945, 161–82, 252–68.

W. G. V. BALCHIN and N. PYE, "The Drought in the South-Western United States", *Weather*, Vol. VIII, 1953, 233–6.

G. B. BARBOUR, "Texas Oil", *G.J.*, C, 1942, 145–55.

12. Canada—East

S. A. SAUNDERS, *Studies in the Economy of the Maritime Provinces*, Macmillan (N.Y.), 1939.

B. V. GUTSELL, *An Introduction to the Geography of Newfoundland*, Canadian Government, Department of External Affairs, 1950.

D. HOAN, "St. Lawrence Seaway", *Canadian G.J.*, Vol. 36, 1948, 53–69.

L. CHEVRIER, "St. Lawrence Seaway and Power Project", *G.J.*, Vol. CXIX, 1953, 400–10.

N. A. DEANSON, "Geographic Factors and Land Use in Ontario", *Canadian G.J.*, Vol. 29, 1944, 80–99.

J. R. RANDALL, "Settlement of the Clay Belt of N. Ontario and Quebec", *Bull. Geog. Soc.*, Philadelphia, Vol. 35, 1937, 53–65.

H. H. LEWIS, "Population of Quebec Province", *Econ. Geog.*, Vol. 16, 1940, 59–68.

B. K. SANDWELL, "The French Canadians", *A.A.A.P.S.S.*, Vol. 253, 1947, 169–75.

Report on Financial and Economic Position of Newfoundland, Cmd. 6849, H.M.S.O., 1946.

S. C. HUDSON, R. A. STUTT, W. VAN VLEIT and J. L. FORSYTH, *Types of Farming in Canada*, Canadian Ministry of Agriculture, 1949.

"Clay Belt of Ontario and Quebec", *G.J.*, XCVI, 78.

E. L. BRUCE, "The Canadian Shield and its Geographic Effects", *G.J.*, XCIII, 1939, 230–9.

"Development of Mineral Resources in Canada", *G.J.*, 99, 1942, 260–66.

J. W. WATSON, "The Pattern of Canada's Post-War Growth", *Geog.*, 39, 1954, 163–75.

13. The Canadian West

Land Utilisation in Southern Alberta, Canadian Government, Department of Agriculture, Economics Division, Publication No. 610.

V. J. MACKIE, "Manitoba Province of Industry", *Canadian G.J.*, Vol. 41, 1950, 167–81.

The Geography of Oil and Natural Gas in Western Canada, Canadian National Railways, Department of Research and Development, 1950.

G. TAYLOR, "British Columbia: A Study in Topographic Control", *G.R.*, Vol. 32, 1942, 372–402.

C. W. Johnson, "Relative Decline of Wheat in the Prairie Provinces of Canada", *Econ. Geog.*, Vol. 24, 1948, 209–16.

R. C. Farrow, "Search for Power in the British Columbia Coast Range", *G.J.*, Vol. CVI, 1945, 89–117.

14. The Canadian North

The Northwest Territories: Administration, Resources, Development, Canadian Government, Bureau of N.W. Territory and Yukon Affairs, 1947.

T. Lloyd, "Oil in the Mackenzie Valley", *G.R.*, Vol. 34, 1944, 275–307

C. A. Dawson (ed.), *The New North-West,* Toronto, 1947.

D. Leechman, "Yukon Territory", *Canadian G.J.*, Vol. 40, 1950, 240–67.

T. Lloyd, "The Mackenzie Waterway: a Northern Supply Route", *G.R.*, Vol. 33, 1943, 415–34.

M. H. Leppard, "The Settlement of Peace River Country", *G.R.*, Vol. 25, 1935, 62–78.

Kirk H. Stone, *Some Geographical Bases for Planning New Alaskan Settlement,* Alaskan Science Conference Reprint.

Mid-Century Alaska, U.S. Department of Interior, Government Printing Office, 1952.

Kirk H. Stone, "Populating Alaska: the United States Phase", *G.R.*, Vol. XLII, 1952, 384–404.

Literary Reading List[1]

General

Rivers of America Series (volumes published on *Hudson, Ohio, Suwanee, St. Lawrence*), Rinehart, N.Y.

G. R. STEWART, *The Storm*, Random House, N.Y.; *Ordeal by Hunger*, Holt, N.Y.; *U.S. 40*, Houghton Mifflin, Boston.

STEPHEN VINCENT BENÉT, *John Brown's Body*, O.UP., 1944.

WALT WHITMAN, *Leaves of Grass*, Modern Library (Harold Hill).

GEOFFREY MOORE (ed.), *The Penguin Book of Modern American Verse*, Penguin.

New England

GLADYS HASTY CARROLL, *As the Earth Turns*, Macmillan, N.Y., 1933.

ANN B. GREEN, *The Lone Winter*, Century, N.Y., 1923.

NATHANIEL HAWTHORNE, *The House of Seven Gables* (1851), Everyman Library.

S. O. JEWETT, *The Country of the Pointed Firs* (1896), Cape, 1929.

J. P. MARQUAND, *H. M. Pulham, Esq.*, Robert Hale, 1948 (and Penguin).

W. D. HOWELLS, *April Hopes*, Harper, N.Y., 1885.

LOUISE DICKINSON RICH, *My Neck of the Woods*, Robert Hale.

UPTON SINCLAIR, *Boston*, Boni, N.Y., 1928.

EDITH WHARTON, *Ethan Frome* (1911), Penguin.

Some of the Poetry of R. W. Emerson, Robert Frost (Cape) and Emily Dickinson (Cape).

New York

JOHN DOS PASSOS, *Manhattan Transfer*, Harper, N.Y., 1925.

Atlantic Coast Plain

ELLEN GLASGOW, *Vein of Iron*, Harcourt Brace, N.Y., 1935; *Barren Ground*, John Murray, 1925.

D. HEYWARD, *Porgy* (1925), Cape.

JULIA PETERKIN, *Scarlet Sister Mary*, Bobbs-Merrill, Indianapolis, 1928; *Black April*, Bobbs-Merrill, N.Y., 1927; *Green Thursday*, Knopf, N.Y., 1924.

THOMAS WOLFE, *Look Homeward Angel*, Heinemann, 1943.

[1] See p. 222, *Note on Availability of Books.*

The Appalachian Mountains

A. CONAN DOYLE, *The Valley of Fear*, John Murray.
JOHN FOX, *The Cumberland Vendetta*, Harper, N.Y., 1896.

Middle West

WILLA CATHER, *My Antonia*, Houghton Mifflin, N.Y., 1918.
THEODORE DREISER, *Sister Carrie* (1900), Liveright, N.Y., 1929.
WALTER HAVINGHURST, *Land of Promise*, Macmillan, N.Y., 1946.
GRAHAM HUTTON, *Mid West At Noon*, Harrap, 1946.
SINCLAIR LEWIS, *Babbitt*, Cape, 1923; *Main Street* (1920), Penguin.
EDGAR L. MASTERS, *Across Spoon River* (1936), Werner Laurie.
UPTON SINCLAIR, *The Jungle*, Werner Laurie, 1906 (and Penguin).
WILLIAM E. WILSON, *Crescent City*, Simon & Schuster, N.Y., 1947.
Poetry of Carl Sandburg (Cape)

Mississippi

W. FAULKNER, *Absolom, Absolom*, Random House, N.Y., 1936.
EDNA FERBER, *Showboat*, Doubleday, N.Y., 1926.
GEORGE GABLE, *The Lovers of Louisiana*, Scribner, N.Y., 1918.
MARK TWAIN, *Life on the Mississippi* (1883), Chatto and Windus.
TENNESSEE WILLIAMS, *Streetcar Named Desire*, Lehmann, 1949.

The South

FRED GIPSON, *Home Place*, Michael Joseph (farming in Texas highlands).
MARGARET MITCHELL, *Gone With The Wind*, Macmillan, 1943.
CAROLINE MILLER, *Lamb in His Bosom*, Harper, N.Y., 1933.
E. M. ROBERTS, *Time of Man*, Viking Press, N.Y., 1926.
ROBERT PENN WARREN, *All the King's Men*, Eyre & Spottiswoode, 1948.
LILLIAN SMITH, *Strange Fruit*, Reynal, N.Y., 1944.

Mountain West

WILLA CATHER, *Death Comes for the Archbishop* (1927), Heinemann.
W. V. T. CLARK, *The Trails of the Cat*, Random House, N.Y., 1949.
C. B. GLASSCOCK, *The Big Bonanza*, Bobbs-Merrill, N.Y., 1931.
WASHINGTON IRVING, *The Adventures of Captain Bonneville*, 1856.
FRANCIS PARKMAN, *Oregon Trail*, O.U.P. and Penguin.
OLE E. ROLVAAG, *Giants in the Earth*, Harper, 1927

Pacific Coast

JADE SNOW WONG, *Fifth Chinese Daughter*, Hurst and Blackett.
JOHN STEINBECK, *Grapes of Wrath*, Heinemann, 1940; *Tortilla Flat*, Penguin.
H. E. BOLTON, *Outpost of Empire*, Knopf, N.Y., 1930
W. O. DOUGLAS, *Of Men and Mountains*, Gollancz.
MARK L. LUTHER, *Boosters*, Bobbs-Merrill, N.Y., 1924.
UPTON SINCLAIR, *Oil!* (1927), Werner Laurie.

Canada

LESLIE ROBERTS, *Canada: The Golden Hinge*, Harrap, 1953.

ERNEST WATKINS, *Prospect of Canada*, Secker and Warburg, 1954.

WILLA CATHER, *Shadows on the Rock* (1931), Cassell.

LOUIS HEMON, *Maria Chapdelaine*, Macmillan, Toronto, 1921.

WILLIAM KIRBY, *The Golden Dog*, Musson, Toronto, 1946.

STEPHEN LEACOCK, *Sunshine Sketches of a Little Town*, Bodley Head and Penguin.

JACK LONDON, *Call of the Wild* (1905), Heinemann.

HUGH MacLENNAN, *Two Solitudes*, Collins, Toronto, 1945.

JOHN D. ROBINS (ed.), *A Pocketful of Canada* (Anthology), Collins, Toronto, 1946.

GABRIEL ROY, *The Tin Flute*, Heinemann, 1948.

S. E. WHITE, *The Blazed Trail*, Doubleday, N.Y., 1921.

Note on Availability of Books

Many of the books and periodicals listed above have not been published in Great Britain. Inquiries concerning books on the U.S.A. and Canada respectively are welcomed, however, by the American Library, 41 Grosvenor Square, W.1, and by Canada House Library, Trafalgar Square, S.W.1. These Libraries lend books free of charge to any resident of Great Britain who applies in person or by post.

Index

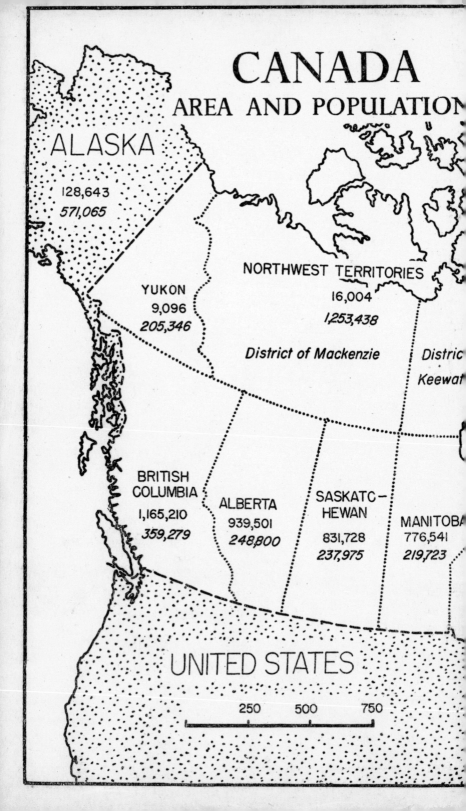

CANADA
AREA AND POPULATION

ALASKA
128,643
571,065

NORTHWEST TERRITORIES
16,004
1,253,438

YUKON
9,096
205,346

District of Mackenzie

Distric

Keewat

BRITISH
COLUMBIA
1,165,210
359,279

ALBERTA
939,501
248,800

SASKATC-
HEWAN
831,728
237,975

MANITOBA
776,541
219,723

UNITED STATES

250   500   750